Patricia Wendorf was b
the Second World War,
ough, which is where s
the bestselling *Patteran*
on her own family history, and of *Leo Days*
Peacefully: in Berlin, received wide critical acclaim.

Also by Patricia Wendorf:

LEO DAYS

The Patteran Trilogy:

LARKSLEVE

BLANCHE

BYE BYE BLACKBIRD

PATRICIA WENDORF

Peacefully: in Berlin

Futura

A Futura Book

First published in Great Britain in 1983
by Hamish Hamilton Ltd, London

This edition published in 1988 by
Futura Publications, a Division of
Macdonald & Co (Publishers) Ltd
London & Sydney

ISBN 0 7088 3742 5

Reproduced, printed and bound in Great Britain by
Hazell Watson & Viney Limited
Member of BPCC plc
Aylesbury Bucks

Futura Publications
A Division of
Macdonald & Co (Publishers) Ltd
Greater London House
Hampstead Road
London NW1 7QX
A Member of Maxwell Pergamon Publishing Corporation plc

This book was written for
my dear sons and grandchildren

Part One

England 1979

The boat train left Nottingham Station at twenty past five in the afternoon. It would call at places with pleasant evocative names like Stowmarket, Cambridge, and Bury St Edmunds. She found that she still remembered the route after twenty-five years. Late March was a little early for continental travel, and she had the compartment all to herself. She watched the blue spring dusk creep across the empty fields, and saw the lights coming on in the little East Anglian towns. She reached for her shoulder bag and opened it: quite unable to resist the obsessional need to check and re-check its contents. She reviewed the tasks she had been obliged to perform before her departure. The Will, deposited with her bank, was the kind of precaution that any middle-aged woman would take before making a journey. Her affairs and her house had been left in scrupulous order. Her goodbyes had been said with what she hoped was a deceptive lack of emotion.

She had left no explanatory letter.

*

The ship was manned by polite young Dutchmen. A steward carried her suitcase down to the cabin and enquired in English: 'Shall I bring morning tea for you madam, or would you prefer coffee?' His manner was that of an impatient nanny towards a slow and uncomprehending child, and she realised that to him she must look quite old. She sat down on the bunk and the mirror above the washbowl threw back her reflection: smooth silver hair, well-cut tweeds, sheepskin jacket. The typical Englishwoman, travelling abroad, unescorted.

The Hook van Holland is not an attractive port, but the cheerful group who disembarked from the Sealink ferry on the following morning gave it an unexpectedly raffish charm. She found herself standing in line among leather clad boys with flowing hair and bandido moustaches, who were hefting guitars and drum-kits through Customs. Their elation touched her. They talked about discos and nightclubs in Amsterdam; about unsuccessful gigs, and their chronic shortage of money. To her surprise they laughed all the time.

The trans-continental express turned out to be a dark green train whose enormous length sneaked around a bend in the line, and out of her vision. She lifted her suitcase in through an open door, and began to hunt for the reserved seat which bore her number.

*

A tall, thin man was already in occupation and displaying the fussy regard for order and cleanliness which marks the travelling German wherever he goes. He put several empty cigarette cartons into the waste-bin, and then he closed the window and turned up the heating to 'FULL'. Before sitting down he scrubbed at the red leather seats with a handful of Kleenex.

'This has to be an East German train,' he complained, 'all their rolling stock is in this filthy condition.' She nodded agreement. It was exactly the sort of complaint that her husband had frequently made about trains in England.

They departed according to schedule: sliding gently away from the port between rows of tall grey ships, at anchor. The man in the corner began to fuss with his luggage. He re-arranged several small parcels, and then folded his raincoat neatly and placed it upon the rack with his rolled umbrella. She tried to rein in her irritation. He had paid for his seat, and with it his freedom to fidget. The briefcase remained near his hand, as a possible future source of annoyance. She gritted her teeth; she suspected that he would turn out to be one of those people who feel compelled to talk to fellow travellers on long journeys.

At last he sat down in the opposite corner, in a seat which was, like her own, labelled RESERVIERT. He opened his lips right on cue. 'So how did you find the crossing?'

'I was quite comfortable. I slept till the steward called me.' Her tone was deliberately cool.

'I hardly slept at all,' he went on, 'such a heavy sea running, and such noise on my side of the ship.' He certainly looked like a man who had had no sleep. With any luck he might doze on the journey. Silver canals were slanting away, ruler straight across bright green fields. The man in the corner ignored the view. He was quite openly reading the labels on her suitcase.

'Frau von Riesbach?' She noticed how his tone had become respectful. 'Nothing so grand I'm afraid,' she said firmly, 'my name is Baumann, no aristocratic pre-fix.' To her annoyance the man's raised eyebrows led her on into further indiscretions. 'Frau von Riesbach is the friend I shall stay with in West Berlin,' she explained. 'I addressed my luggage to her for safety.'

'Very wise,' he remarked, 'and so how do you like Berlin?'

'I don't know. This will be my first visit.'

'Berlin is my home town,' he told her. 'I was born in Schöneberg. But of course you will have already concluded that I am German'; and of course, she had: in spite of his tweeds and his hush-puppy brogues. Age, early fifties she thought. He displayed that curious German mixture of over-familiarity and good manners; the slight American drawl in his speech was intriguing; a very ill man, she concluded. His sunken eyes and bad colour had little to do with his lack of sleep on last night's crossing. He had the frail air of the recently convalescent.

She picked up her book and put on her reading glasses. She hoped he would take the hint.

'I see you read Thomas Mann,' he began again, 'now I find that interesting. Mann foretold the fate of the German people you know. Have you read *Doktor Faustus*?'

She took off her glasses and stared at him. 'Yes,' she said shortly, 'I've read it.'

'Ah,' his voice became urgent, 'but have you really understood the deeper significance of the story?'

'I think so.'

He relaxed against his seat, as if the small exchange had tired him, 'And so what is your conclusion?' he asked wearily. 'How do you English see us? I assume from your voice that you are English. Be truthful now: after all, you read Thomas Mann.'

She slammed the book shut. 'That's hardly fair. The fact that I read Mann means nothing. I simply enjoy a good solid read sometimes. But I also find pleasure in reading Rilke: so what does that tell you?'

'Ach, Rilke. That pansy poet! At least our respected novelist was well-named. But your opinion now, Mrs Baumann. Do not evade the issue.'

She looked down at her drumming fingers, 'What do you want me to say?' she asked him. 'The war ended thirty-four years ago, why can't you let it rest there. I assume that you want to rake over cold ashes. I find that a pretty pointless exercise, and so, if you will forgive me saying so, I should think would you.'

He leaned back in his seat and watched her through half-closed eyes. 'Strange lady,' he mocked, 'strange English lady who tells me her name is Baumann. Now that is a good old German name, is it not?'

She felt her facial muscles tighten, and willed herself to relax. 'No mystery attached to my name,' she said lightly, 'my husband was German.'

'Was?'

'He died last year.'

'So you are a widow,' his voice became gentle, 'you do not say that word. Does it trouble you that much?'

For a moment she didn't know whether to laugh or cry, or simply get up and leave the compartment. 'My mother told me never to talk to strangers on trains,' she said, 'she must have been thinking of someone like you.'

He grinned. 'My seat is reserved Mrs Baumann, and, so I see, is yours. We shall be forced to travel together for at least another eleven hours. We could have a very interesting conversation if you will permit it.'

'I think,' she said, 'if you don't mind, I would rather catch up on my reading.'

*

'How old was your husband?'

'Fifty-three.'

'May I ask you the nature of his illness.'

'He died of a cardiac arrest.'

'Ah yes. That must have been a very sudden disappearance.'

'Not really. He had been ill for many years. I should have expected it to happen. Been prepared.'

'But you were not?'

'No.'

He said unexpectedly, 'I too have an English wife. We live in Devonshire.' He managed to make the statement sound both significant and yet comforting, as if the nationality of his wife was a link she could not refuse to acknowledge.

His name, he told her, was Jürgen Hecht. His wife was called Helen. Their young daughter was ten years old.

They were blissfully happy.

*

Breakfast was served by a steward who wore a crumpled white jacket. She settled herself at a window placing, and Jürgen Hecht slipped into the opposite seat without asking permission. He was still grumbling about the state of the train and the slipshod service. 'East German staff, I suppose,' he muttered, 'that fellow has slept in his clothes. God only knows what sort of breakfast they'll give us.'

The coffee was black and scalding, but the rolls were the texture of cotton-wool, and the butter unsalted. Two greasy fried eggs were served on a portion of soggy, pale toast: but they ate every crumb, and then called for more coffee. Half an hour later, having paid their separate bills, they raised their elbows to allow the steward to remove the cloth from the table. 'Do you want us to move?' asked Jürgen Hecht.

'Stay as long as you wish,' the man shrugged his unconcern, 'we shall be serving lunch at midday.'

'In that case,' said Jürgen Hecht, 'can we have some more coffee?'

They were travelling at great speed. When the wheels skimmed over the points her coffee slopped over; Jürgen Hecht filled a briar pipe and began to smoke it. 'So where did you meet your husband,' he asked, 'was it in the war?'

She said unhappily, because she had shared a meal with him, 'Look here, if you don't mind, I would rather not talk about it.'

'I really would like to know,' he persisted; 'it is not just,' he searched for the right expression, 'idle curiosity on my part.'

'Where did you learn to speak English?' she asked suddenly.

He looked nonplussed. 'My plane was shot down. The Americans caught me.'

'Wouldn't you also prefer to forget the war, in that case?'

'Because I am German?' His voice was bitter.

'You are twisting my words Mr Hecht. I don't much like that.' She slammed down her cup in annoyance. 'What do you want from me, anyway. Answers? I can't give you any.'

'I think you can,' he said slowly, 'there is something strange in your face when you mention my country; I think you have a direct line to the knowledge I am seeking. You have thought deeply about the subject; and you read Thomas Mann and Rilke.'

She shivered suddenly, and then she laughed. 'Perhaps this crazy train will crash and solve all our problems.'

'And you would welcome that?'

'Well, no,' she said, colouring slightly, 'not really. An accident always seems to involve so many other people. That was not what I meant.'

'What did you mean then? You seem to be saying that you would not find death unwelcome.'

'You are interrogating me now, Mr Hecht. Please stop it.' He bowed slightly. 'My apologies Mrs Baumann,' his tone was sardonic. 'I was not SS I assure you, I was a bomber pilot.'

'And you crashed in France?' He nodded.

'My husband was taken prisoner in France,' she blurted, 'The Canadians caught him. There were several prisoner-of-war camps in my part of England.' She smiled, for the first time that morning. 'You may find this hard to believe, Mr Hecht, but I was a very romantic girl in those days.'

England 1947

The prisoner of war camp lies in the green heart of England; deep in hunting country. From their compound the Germans observe that the farmers and gentry ride out together on white winter mornings to hunt for the fox. The farmers are dressed in cords and hacking jackets; the gentry wear breeches and scarlet coats. They sit straight-backed in the saddle: their eyes fixed on some invisible quarry beyond the dark blue line of the trees.

Kurt Baumann is a man who knows about horses. He moves close to the barbed-wire fence to observe the English riders as they pass beneath the bare branches. The glossy rumps of the horses are steaming lightly in the frosty air: they are moving quietly now, four abreast, along the broad rideway that bisects the woodland.

After six years spent on ships and in prison camps he can still feel the slip of the reins in his fingers, and the power of moving horse flesh between his knees. He raises his eyes to take in the sight of the stately English riders and he is shaken with envy, and such a longing for freedom that he can hardly bear it. He never allows himself to anticipate the day when the gates will open and he will be free to walk into the world again. Kurt Baumann believes that if you long for something too fiercely, you never achieve it.

*

They are guarded at first by soldiers with loaded rifles: a joke, since not one of them ever makes a token attempt at escape. The British take a second look and decide that so much manpower can be better employed on the farms of England.

Kurt Baumann does not expect to be included among those prisoners who are to be permitted to labour for their captors. He had been involved in a fight with a fellow prisoner, and has recently spent three weeks in solitary confinement, on a bread and water diet. He is unable to speak one word of English, and is considered to be the most truculent member of his unit. But he puts his name on the list, anyway.

To his surprise, he is selected. He is taken before his Commandants, both English and German, and warned that the reputation of his nation will depend on his good behaviour and the respect he shows to the English farmer, who is to be his employer, host, and unofficial gaoler.

'Learn some English,' the German officer warns him. But he has no intention of speaking the enemy's lisping language: he has acquired his own set of graphic signals, and among the guards, two fingers have served him very well.

Together with Manfred Weiss he is sent to a farm called Hobart's. They have been vetted and passed as dependable men, who will be allowed to live in with the farmer's family.

*

There are two farms in the valley. Chilton's spreads out across the lower reaches; Hobart's is tucked up neatly underneath the hill. A narrow lane hedged with hawthorn marks the boundary between them. The milk lorry calls once a day. On Fridays a man in a van collects the eggs; the postwoman comes up on horseback every morning. The traffic across the wolds is light.

The Hobarts are old; their bodies are twisted like ancient trees, and they have begun to look alike, as some couples do after many years spent together. The decision to employ two German prisoners-of-war has been taken only after many weeks of anxious deliberation.

The master of Chilton's farm is younger; he has served as an officer in the local Home Guard. He has never fired a live bullet in anger, but all the same, he distrusts the Germans, and refuses to use them as a source of labour. George Chilton employs a land-army girl called Cathy. The land-army labour is cheap: and a girl works as well as a man – as long as you watch her.

Catherine Wyatt had left her job in a city office, to do her bit for England, and search for her own true romance. All she has found on the land that summer is an aching back and a handful of blisters. But the English are a stoical race, and she soldiers on through haytime and harvest, with her virginity and her belief in romantic love still intact.

At threshing-time the Chiltons and Hobarts agree to combine their work force, in order to form a more efficient team; and so, on this one and only occasion, the English and German farmworkers come together.

*

By mid-October the sun hangs low in the morning sky, and the air is sharp like new wine. Berries of scarlet hip and crimson hawthorn drip from the hedges; and the stooked corn, heavy and golden, awaits the drum of the thresher.

The machine had pulled onto Chilton's land on the previous evening. It stands close up against the roughly stacked corn, and the Englishmen wait beside it. The two Germans arrive in the field as soon as the milking is finished. George Chilton starts up the motor, and the prisoners take up their positions on top of the stack. They will not need any spoken orders. They are old hands at this job.

The Germans work as a team, lifting the stooks to the man on the thresher who severs the binder twine and feeds the loosened straw into the drum. One man looks after the chaff hole: and another carries the loaded grain sacks across to the trailer. It is hot and dusty work. At dinner-time the Englishmen form a semi-circle with straw-bales: they sit together, a close, exclusive company. The Germans retreat to the far edge of the field.

The land-army girl has not been told that the blond haired men are prisoners.

Cathy Wyatt dispenses hot tea and sandwiches to the threshers without needing to take in faces. She is as close to giving up hope as she will ever be. These men are middle-aged, long-married, dull. The recruiting posters have promised her magic: she has dreamed of romance in the greenwood.

She has had so little in her life that summer; had hoped for so much more. The men who sit apart by the hedge annoy her. Uneven ground is hard on the feet that blister no matter how often she changes her woollen land-army socks. As she walks towards them carrying the heavy basket, the younger man lifts his chin from his chest, pushes the thick blond hair from his forehead, and feigns an extravagant, wide-eyed amazement. She pours tea into thick brown mugs and avoids his eyes; she thinks she has met his kind before in the city: wolf whistling on street corners at good girls whose curfew is set for nine. Or slipping a casual arm across the back of a cinema seat, as soon as the house lights go down. Well, to say met is perhaps not strictly true. She has observed such boys with mixed delight and repulsion: nose pressed up against the shop window, resisting the goodies just out of her reach. She has a father at home (ex-Army), who waits for her by the garden gate every evening; a mother who charts her every movement, mariner-fashion. There had not been much room to spare that springtime, but somehow she had managed to slip between them: escape to this Happy Valley. This geriatric Paradise. This Old-folks Haven.

*

The land girl goes to church on a Sunday morning. Kurt Baumann sees her cycling down the lane, that rust coloured hair streaming over her shoulders. He asks Manfred, 'Well – what about her?'

'Pretty face. But I prefer big girls.' Manfred looks on English girls as out-of-season game. He has a wife in München to whom he is faithful, in thought and deed. 'These English are much too skinny for my taste.'

Kurt Baumann is beginning, against his will, to understand English. Whenever the Hobarts speak of the girl, he listens.

'She's present at Morning Service, I notice,' the old lady comments. The Hobarts have a bachelor son who is a schoolmaster in a neighbouring village; one of these days Ralph Hobart will inherit the farm. 'Our Ralph will be home this week-end. We must see to it that he goes to church.' Her little black eyes flick a challenge across the supper-table, 'make a very good wife, she would – for a farmer's son.'

Sometimes Kurt catches himself thinking in English. He finds it a devious language: more subtle than German, more set about with traps, which will allow the same things to be said, but in too many different ways. The English have a saying: 'I cannot make up my mind.' It puzzles him. 'Entschliessen', says Manfred, is the equivalent in German. 'Decision', he knows where he is with that.

'I cannot make up my mind.' He shouts the words out loud,

standing alone in the ploughed October field, waving his arms like some wild and angry bird-scarer.

The girl is a stone in his shoe. Dust in his eyes. A thorn in his finger.

*

Sometimes they let him take the shotgun out in the evenings. A pheasant or a rabbit will be a welcome change, they say, and old man Hobart has grown too stiff to stalk the woods for game. Kurt is gradually shedding his old truculence: lowering his fists from the habitual, threatening stance he has found necessary for survival, at most, at least, in the past seven years.

Autumn evenings in this valley are drowsy, hypnotic. There is a smell of burning leaves on the rising mist, and the trees and hedgerows are full of tiny rustling sounds, and violet shadows. If he treads softly, he tells himself it is because he is unwilling to alarm the pheasants. It is so still that every slightest sound is magnified. As he walks in the lane that divides the farmsteads he can hear the trapdoors on Chilton's poultry sheds being dropped and fastened. He moves towards the five-barred gate and waits: and soon he sees her, bandaged hands in pockets, making her last, late round of the day.

She is wearing washed-out cotton trousers and a shrunken yellow sweater. Manfred is mistaken: she is by no means skinny. Her hair is tied back with a ribbon. In the fading light it looks more brown than red. He longs to reach out a hand to touch it, but caution, and the heavy shotgun on his arm, deter him.

Now it is his turn to be the watcher. He knows that this girl has looked at him in the threshing field, peeping sideways from under that mane of hair. He had lifted the stooks a little higher then; rippled the muscles in his arms; knowing she watched him.

His chest feels warm, the way it had when the new-born foal had come to life in his hands, full five minutes after old man Hobart had proclaimed it dead. She too is hardly born yet: she has that same look about her. Struggling, and yet at the same time, listening out, in case the grown-ups should catch her treading forbidden ground.

The fear in her face, when she becomes aware of his presence, is a pain he hasn't been expecting. When she starts to run he calls her back. Strange how the English words will drop into his head when he really needs them. She hesitates; sniffs the air for danger, and scenting none, she moves slowly out towards him. But not too close: she will leave a wide space between her body and that five-barred gate.

He nods politely, the way he always did to girls at home, in Mechtenhausen. He says, 'Good-evening,' carefully. She looks surprised, almost accusing. 'I thought you couldn't speak any English.'

'I speak little bit. Understand sehr gut.'

'You didn't speak in the threshing field.'

'Englishman see us there. Better we not talk. Make much trouble.'

The shotgun is pulling her eyes down from his face. Suddenly he can feel her fear. A German with a gun. Swiftly, he shifts the angle; lets the barrel point away towards the trees. He will keep her with him as long as he is able: what are the English words?

'You have broken hands?'

'Blisters,' she says, shrugging away the shame of it. 'I had never used an axe or shovel you see, until I came here; or carried heavy buckets.'

He cannot comprehend it. 'Why you work in this place. You not farm girl I damn sure.'

'I worked in the city: in a Government office. It bored me, and so I joined the Land Army.' Defensively she thrusts her hands into her trouser pockets; she begins to move away from the gate, and into the shadows. 'I must go now,' she says, 'they won't like it if they catch me talking to you.'

*

'A dictionary is what you want,' the farmer tells him, 'learn a few more words, so that we have a better understanding.' Kurt's already jutting jaw moves out a little further. He takes the book, says thank you, and tosses it into the bottom drawer of the dressing-table. He does not want English words, has never, for that matter, needed very many German ones. Especially with girls.

The dunes have been his happy hunting ground in the old days. That long white empty beach at Swinemünde on a Sunday afternoon. A cold wind blowing off the Baltic; finding some shelter in the marram grass, and who cared what the Hitler Youth got up to at the week-end. He'd only looked out for some warm girl who didn't fear her father. Who wanted what he wanted. Who needed words?

At home he'd always had a special place to take them: the girls he fell in love with. In England the straw stack seems a likely spot: the one he'd helped to build at threshing time.

At first he thinks she won't come with him.

'Gehen wir spazieren?' he asks her; always the opening gambit. But he can see that the German words alarm her. 'We go for walk?' he repeats, in English, and this time she smiles.

The moonlight spills silver over the fields, arousing the dormant lover in him. He has not walked in moonshine, with a girl at his side, since the summer of '43. But this English girl is hardly dressed for seduction. She is still wearing the corduroy riding breeches and thick green woollen sweater, which is standard land-army winter issue. She has made no special effort for him. No bouncing curls; no tight-fitting dress; no silk stockings.

He walks her innocently across the whitening meadows, but in the end they come up to the straw stack, as he had meant them to. He sets two strawbales up against the stack, but not too close together. She sits on the very edge of hers, poised for instant flight, even though there is no safe place for her to run to.

He begins to roll up a cigarette, but the thin paper sticks to his sweating fingers. When he speaks the words come out harsh, and louder than he intended.

'My name is Kurt Baumann.'

'I'm Catherine Wyatt – but people call me Cathy.'

'How many years have you?'

'I'm nineteen.'

Relief expels the breath he hasn't known that he is holding. Nineteen is just acceptable. He had feared she might be younger.

'I – six and twenty. Three years on ship; three years prisoner of war.'

'You were in the German Navy?'

'Ja. Navy.' He repeats the new word a few times to fix it in his mind.

'I am Obergefreiter. Erste Klasse.'

'Is that in submarines?'

A word he doesn't know: Ach Gott what can she mean?

'Bitte?' he asks politely.

'U-boats. Were you in U-boats?'

'Nein. I am mit ship pulls bomb from water.'

'Minesweeper. Is that what you want to say?'

'Ja. Ist richtig.' Suddenly he wants to tell her about it. Hours spent adrift in the North Sea, in an open boat: men dying around him. Shipmates. Kameraden. The freezing cold: the ice inside his nostrils. He pushes away the hair that curls around his ears, letting her see the broken skin and scars.

'Frostbite?' she asks.

'Ja. Feet broken too. Ist not so bad.' He makes his voice sound casual, 'Other men die. I strong.' He pinches out the half-smoked cigarette and places it carefully in the tin that holds his tobacco and papers.

'Sea ist nicht gut. On land ist viel besser. On land ist farm. I walk on grass; birds sing; I see nice girl.'

'You like English girls?'

How should he know? She is the first one he has managed to get this close to. 'Not talk English girl. Ist streng verboten. In camp – Deutsche Offizier tell – not talk English girl – make much trouble.'

'So what about me?'

'No man see us. You good girl I think. Not tell to farmer.'

The talking is proving pleasanter than he'd expected. Necessary too, in her case: she is a foreigner and wary. Even by moonlight he can see that her hands are raw and blistered: the fingernails broken.

'Why you work on farm? I think is not gut job for you. You not manage heavy work. You are,' he searches for the appropriate word, 'you are lady.' She turns a blazing face on him: one he has not seen before. Ach, these proud and touchy English!

'I joined the Land Army,' she says, 'because I wanted to.' She is emphasising each word with a stabbing finger: 'Of my own free will, you understand. I wanted a different sort of life. I wanted freedom.' He has heard about free will. 'Freie Wille' they had called it, in Germany in 1939. He has never had much to do with it himself; cannot remember having exercised so rare a privilege. Ah well: he cannot argue with her. Ask her the vital question now: why not?

'You have lover at home?' She looks surprised, but he has checked the word in the dictionary in case he needs it. Her tone is cool.

'I have a friend. He writes to me sometimes.'

'Ach! That is not lover.' He watches her closely now: she has no pride, no thrown-back shoulders when she speaks of men.

'You allow to kiss with him?' She does not answer right away, instead, she plaits straw between her ruined fingers. 'Sometimes,' she says at last.

He thinks she lies: is damn sure she lies. He thinks he has met her kind before: she will be the sort who pleads no when she really means yes. But these prim little girls who profess to fear their fathers usually turn out to be the best prospects, in the long run.

'You allow to kiss with me?'

He has found 'allow' a useful word to know in English. He has spent the past few months in finding out how much the English will allow him: and now, like a magic sesame, it brings her to his side. She makes the move towards him: eyes shut, just like Marlene Dietrich in the movies. She touches him, light as a butterfly, on the mouth, her lips firmly closed. He almost laughs.

'That is what you call kissing?'

'Didn't I do it right?'

'Come Engländerin,' he whispers, vowing her safety, 'I show you how is richtig kissing.'

The moon is tangled in among the elm trees, and he can hear a dog-fox barking out in the hills. He breathes in sharply through flared nostrils, aware of the English girl's anxiety and her utter stillness. Calmly, he pulls her towards him: but the violent tremor that shakes her alarms him. Her hair has changed colour again: is black in the moonlight. He pushes a strand of it back from her forehead: gentles her with the soft words he would have used with a nervous mare. 'Is OK' he says, 'I not bad man: not hurt you.'

'I know,' she mutters, 'I know it –'

'But you not kiss with German ja?'

The taunt brings on the old defiant reaction that seems to be her hallmark. She moves towards him deliberately, eyes shut, lips pressed delicately together. He bends his head and puts his arms around her: and now his concern is more with her instruction in the art, than with his own satisfaction.

She will not, no matter how hard he presses, allow him beyond her lips. Her teeth are locked tightly together; he raises his head and begins to stroke her jaw lightly to ease the spasm. Her ignorance of the proper procedure is not, as he has at first suspected, assumed to inflame him. She truly, at nineteen years, is not yet a woman: does not know what to do.

He could have explained it politely in German: all he can say in English is, 'Please – please open mouth.' She is helpless with sudden mirth: she slumps weakly towards him, and he takes her full weight on his arm. 'Oh,' she gasps, 'You sound just like a dentist.'

He judges the moment, and catches her lips on a wide wave of laughter: she struggles against him, and then she is still. Her arms creep around his neck, and her fingers are deep in the hair at the nape of his neck: she pulls his face downwards towards her. Well, some gestures at least, he thinks, have come naturally to her. She is the first one to move away: he releases her slowly and takes two paces backwards. Her face has a naked look in the moonlight.

'Was it better that time?' she asks.

'Ach ja! That was good: was richtig kiss.'

It was more than good. He is forced to admit this disturbing fact as he walks back to Hobart's. The dog-fox is silent now, and the moon is untangling itself from the elm trees; his thoughts have the bitter clarity of the moonlight. The kiss has uprooted him, has laid bare his intended chicanery: it had not been the common or garden variety of contact that he had envisaged. This collision of mouth on mouth has set a seal. On what exactly, or whom, he is not quite certain.

In France, and in certain ports at home, there had been special houses set aside, marked 'Reserviert. Nur für die Deutsche Wehrmacht', where a sailor on leave might visit in safety. He had never cared much for the looks of those weary young-old girls, in their shiny black satin, and beer stained underclothing. He preferred country girls with clean faces, and sweet smelling hair. Amazingly, he has retained his standards of fastidiousness: and a certain innocence. He has never, in his life, paid for a woman.

*

Kurt has never had much time for books, but lately the dictionary is always in his hand. Cathy uses fancy words he never hears at Hobart's. She talks to him about music: asks how he feels about Beethoven. 'Pretty gut,' he says, using his latest English phrase. Well, at least he's heard of him. But when she says she admires Shostakovitch, he is lost. It sounds Russian, so he looks upset, and she apologises. Music, for him, has been the accordion he plays at village dances, when it is getting late, and his mother requests the old melodies that always make her cry.

This Cathy says that recently she read Goethe in translation, but hadn't understood him very well. He has also heard of him, of course. But hell! who needed Goethe? *Mein Kampf* has been the standard reading in his school.

Kultur is what she has: capital 'K' and he no good at any of it. He knows what he is good at. That foal. Leave it, they said: but he couldn't let it go like that. Pretty, that chestnut colour. Perfectly formed. Head lolling, legs sprawling, hanging limp and lifeless in his hands: he had rubbed and pummelled, breathed and sucked, willed the life into it. He had wrapped it in his jacket, and warmed it against his body until it lived and opened its eyes for him. She is the same: no life in her until he loved her, and that is something else that he is good at.

'You have the best composers in your country,' she tells him, 'the soundest philosophers too. Have you read Schopenhauer or Kant?' In the Training School in Kiel, he stripped a machine gun down as fast as his instructor. He coped with mathematics as well as any city boy. He does not yet have sufficient words in English, to defend himself against her. But he is learning.

Her mind is unknown territory for him: God knows what goes on there. She has thoughts that he considers women shouldn't have. Politics are for the men. The rights and wrongs.

'I suppose,' she says, looking at him with that scared, defensive air that is her habit, 'I suppose you were safe enough when Hitler came to power? Being the handsome blue-eyed, blond haired Aryan type, I mean.'

He suspects her of mocking him. She is still angry with him because he told her she couldn't kiss like a woman.

Belsen, Dachau, Auschwitz. She has to drag that up. A sensitive girl, one who considered his feelings, would have avoided that particular subject. He tries to turn the discussion, but he is finding out that, once started, she is impossible to dissuade.

'Lies,' he shouts, 'all lies. Propaganda from your Churchill.' He folds his arms tight across his chest to conceal their trembling. She is looking at him as though she pities him his denial.

'How can you pretend to believe such rubbish?' she asks. He is growing angry: and will not be patronised by her.

'Your soldiers. They stand over us with guns – make us to watch that film of Belsen. Some of our men get sick – they weep – want to run outside. Watch it, your officers tell us. See what your people have done to the Jews.'

He grabs her thin wrists (don't break them), and looks her straight in the eye.

'I tell you true. When I am child I go with my parents, shopping in city of Stettin. We always buy clothes in Jewish shop. Jew is kind to small child: gives me pencil or small penknife: little present. How shall I hurt these people who are good to me?'

His inquisitor is temporarily confused.

'Well,' she says, twisting a strand of hair in her nervous fingers, 'I suppose it's hardly fair to blame you personally for what happened.'

'But you blame me,' he blurts, 'you, my only friend. You put this shame on my head. How can you speak?' he demands, 'You were not there. You do not know about war, you only read about it.' He takes a wide step away from her. 'I not talk with you anymore. We have not understanding between us.'

She is clever in all the ways he most despises. But still, he cannot leave her. He sees her bright head moving down in Chilton's fields, and the white blur of her bandaged, inefficient hands: and he is back again that night at his old station. Waiting in the moonlight, beside the five-barred gate.

*

The first frosts come to the valley, and the straw stack no longer affords them shelter. There is derelict cottage at the far edge of Chilton's acres: a warm refuge, since it is used for storing fodder. They begin to meet there every evening. The fraternisation ban has been lifted, but she is still uneasy in his company. Her coolness annoys him: it is he thinks a deliberate ploy to lower his pride. He will try her out: see if his hand has lost its old cunning. Before she can stop him he has unfastened the top buttons on her land Army shirt.

Suddenly, she is yelling: pushing him backwards so that he loses his footing, and falls heavily onto the hay bales. 'What the hell do you think you are doing?' she cries. 'You're pretty cheeky aren't you?'

'Cheeky?' He straightens his jacket and frowns.

'You are not the only one who studies the dictionary,' she snaps; 'I also look up the relevant words. "Frech" is what you are.' He throws back his head and roars his pleasure. 'Ja! du hast recht. Ich bin frech. I-am-cheeky. All German girls tell me same thing.' He slaps his thigh in delight. 'I-am-cheeky. Ist gut ja? You like it?'

Her face is a pale blur in the moonlight. 'Whether I like it or not,' she says firmly, 'is beside the point. One thing might lead to another: and you will vanish like the summer days. What happens to me then?' She sounds like his mother. He is earnest, small boy, pleading.

'We only make us little bits happy. That is not wrong.'

'Yes it is.' She is strong, parental. 'I am going in now. No, don't come with me. I don't think I trust you anymore.'

He is upset: he will show it. 'I not touch you Cathy, if you make me that order.' She lingers beside him a moment; he hangs his head for shame. She relents, as he knows she is bound to. 'Well,' she says slowly, 'you don't have to take it that far. But you are too sure of yourself, you know. You take too much for granted.'

She looks so demure in her high-buttoned shirt, he is bound to believe her. No girl has ever refused him before. Clouds scud across the moon, allowing her pity to seep in the darkness to where he is sitting, obediently untouching.

'When I saw you that first time, in the threshing field, I didn't know right away that you were a German.'

'Who has tell you this?'

'The Chiltons. They issued warnings. Talked about disloyalty. Treated me like a child who needed to be told about bogey-men.'

'Bogey-men?'

She moves across to where he is sitting; she reaches for his hand and holds it in both of hers. She speaks to him like someone who has bad news to tell, and seeks some way of breaking it gently. 'When the air-raid sirens sounded in the night, my brother and I slept underneath the kitchen table. In 1940 I was eleven years old: the Germans were the bogey-men of my childhood.'

'And now?'

'You are the only German I have ever come face to face with. If only you were ugly I could hold my grudge against you.'

*

He has always had a conscience. Not the Lutheran variety approved of by the elders of the Church, in Mechtenhausen, but his own personal gradation of sins that he can never contemplate committing. Girls are fair game: they always have ample opportunity to say no to him, although this Cathy is the first to take advantage of his generosity. He will never, willingly, make a woman cry. Lies? Well bending the truth a little to suit his convenience, does no harm. He has a hair-trigger temper. Dislikes taking orders. Is utterly, foolishly, loyal to kameraden. He never gives up on causes that other people say are lost. He will still be in there, hanging on with toes and eyelids, long after he has forgotten how it all began. But how shall he judge this situation;

this girl. Her language (a soft mutter of tongue behind teeth) will only come easily to him when in her presence. English, for him, has become the language of love: but it is also the speech of deceit and betrayal.

The problem comes between him and his sleep.

*

The tractor's wheels have left deep ruts in the lane. He treads warily, feeling the ice splinter under his feet. Early December, and already a rime of frost silvers the elm trees, and turns the cows' breath white. There is a quality about these days and nights that is unmistakeably English. 'There's a poachers' moon tonight, Kurt,' old man Hobart tells him. He likes the expression: the feel of it on his tongue. There in the lane, in the winter dusk, he moans softly in his indecision.

In the copse, he knows he will find partridge and pheasant sitting, thicker than leaves on the ground.

It is all so available to him. Spread out underneath his fingers: there for the taking.

The pheasants always fall to his first shot. Lately he has needed to catalogue his skills: marking them up, keeping a tally, measuring them against her claims to Kultur: her bid for superiority over him. The money he will collect when the game birds are sold in the Christmas market will buy them a pair of wedding rings. 'We could get married,' he might say to her.

He had thought about marriage once before, with a girl called Valli: the postmaster's only daughter in Swinemünde. Blonde, she had been, with long brown legs and very little conversation. All through the war he has carried an image, of himself, married, a solid burgher, a farmer with hectares of his own. His wife will work at his side: she will be obedient to him. She will, of course, be German. This sibilant English language continues to give him trouble: it is not in his nature to speak quietly, the way she does. 'You bark: you growl,' Cathy tells him, 'too loud, too self-assertive. When you say you love me, say it softly.'

Girls expect to be told that they are loved: it is part of the ritual courtship, no more, no less. But this one arouses compassion in him, equally with lust. A combination, so far, quite unknown to him. The responsibility for her weighs heavily on him.

She says she loves him as if she were handing over her immortal soul.

*

They need permission to marry. He from the British Commandant in the camp, and she from her father.

Her home lies twenty miles beyond the limit that he is allowed to travel. She hides the guilty blue patches on his tunic and trousers, under a raincoat she has 'borrowed' from a peg on the stable wall. She hustles him onto the bus. 'Don't speak a word,' she warns, 'and no one will guess that you're not English.'

Her father's house is built of red brick: it has white bay-windows and a brown front door. The houses along the road stand close together, joined in pairs, like inseparable married couples. He takes this to be an omen. Kurt Baumann causes disbelief and consternation on his first appearance in Kingsbridge. The Wyatts are sure that he is prospecting for a little light entertainment, and that his intentions are bound to be dishonourable. But amazement, for once, has rendered them speechless, and so the initiative is lost. This German has tapped an unsuspected vein of rebellion in Cathy, and she now makes her once-in-a-lifetime gesture of defiance, and thumbs her nose at the world.

'I mean to go with him to Germany,' she informs her parents, 'married – or not married.'

Recognising implacability when they see it, they are obliged to sign her over.

They are married before a Registrar, on a frosty January morning. He wears his best prisoner's uniform. She wears a blue coat. This time his visit to her home is legal, approved by the Military who have granted him permission to marry. 'Is the girl pregnant then?' The officer asked him. Before he could answer 'No-sir' he knew he would not be believed.

Her bedroom makes him feel awkward, and he is not usually a clumsy man. A young girl's room. Pink rugs and curtains, rose taffeta eiderdown, ruffles and flounces. A doll and a teddy-bear sit in an armchair, looking like old inhabitants whose tenure has been secure long before his time. The books are everywhere. He picks up one or two when she isn't looking.

Once, in Mechtenhausen, a girl left a ladder for him, up against her bedroom window, making the whole business a matter of some urgency. 'Out before daylight mind,' she had warned him, 'before my father gets up and finds the ladder.' In England it will be different. No need for such indecent haste now that he is a husband.

At bedtime, he spends ten considerate minutes in conversation with her parents. He has taken advice from Manfred on the delicate matter of honeymoon protocol.

His own nightly ritual, married or single, never varies. He removes his pocket-watch and lays it down on the dressing-table, next to her hairbrush. Then follows his penknife, a few coins, a comb. His shirt and jacket receive a coathanger apiece. But it is his trousers that merit the most attention. He folds them carefully across the wicker stool, pockets emptied: creases sharply aligned. His shoes, he sets neatly side by side, beneath the bookcase. She watches him, wide-eyed from the bed.

As he switches off the light, she begins to giggle softly, 'I never guessed,' she says, 'that you were so damned tidy.'

Part Two

1979

The trans-continental express, said the steward, was running exactly to schedule: they crossed the German-Dutch border at exactly five to eleven that morning. Passport control at the frontier was swift and efficient.

'It won't be so pleasant at Helmstedt,' warned Jürgen Hecht, 'I hear that the East Germans hold this train for an hour, while they search for defectors.' He looked out of the window. 'It seems strange to be back in Germany again.'

'How long has it been?' she asked him.

'Eleven years,' he said thickly: and then with an effort, 'but we are getting away from the story. You married a German in 1948 – what then?'

'He was repatriated. He could have stayed on in England; but he had this burning compulsion to go back. God knows why!'

'Yes. It was pretty horrific in those days. I returned to Berlin in '48. People were almost starving. The Russians blockaded the city – remember. The British were airlifting food to us for several months.'

'I remember,' she sighed. 'After he left I went home to my parents. The Land Army found me a job on a market-garden in Kingsbridge; I wrote off to the Foreign Office, applying for a military visa to enter the British zone of West Germany – and then settled down to wait. I waited for quite a long time.' She smiled. 'I was trying hard to behave like a married woman; I had a ring on my finger, and we had spent two nights together: but somehow I felt abandoned. It was as if I had dreamed the whole unlikely story. I had known him for exactly ten weeks.'

'Most ex-prisoners rushed into marriage,' said Jürgen, 'we were asserting our right to take an action that hadn't been ordered by some military tribunal. I too, got married in 1948, to the girl next door: old sweetheart; all that stuff. It was a disaster. I divorced her sixteen years later.'

'But you re-married.'

'Ah yes. But with Helen it is different. She is English. Have you noticed how good are these German-English connections? But of course you have.'

'I almost missed my connection,' she said, 'I wrote to him in English, he replied in German. You can't imagine the misunderstandings we had on paper.'

'You could not have known what he had to face on his return. We ourselves could hardly believe it. I had been a bomber pilot: I knew very well what war looked like: but when I first saw Berlin I sat down and wept.' The lines in Jürgen Hecht's face grew deeper. 'We came back to Germany in a curious frame of mind,' he said heavily, 'chastened: whipped: defeated; but you must remember that many of us were young men. The sap was still green in us: our ambitions were still intact, if a little dented. But what about you Mrs Baumann? It must have taken courage to marry a German in those days.'

'I don't know,' she said thoughtfully, 'I don't really think it was very brave – more like bravado. My parents, you see, had been very strict. I was not allowed to talk to a man who wore uniform, or stay out late, or go dancing. I joined the Land Army as a respectable means of escape, and I think I probably married Kurt in much the same spirit. I loved him. Dear God, how I loved him! But at the same time, I imagined that I was proving myself to be capable of making a serious moral judgement. Well, I had picked a hot potato out of the pan, but at that stage of course, I didn't know it. I can remember saying goodbye to him at the gates of the prison camp, and thinking he was already somewhere else. To return to Germany was all he really wanted, at that time. Marriage to me had been incidental; a kind of romantic aberration on his part.'

February 1948

It has to pour with rain that morning: long veils of moisture sweeping across the valley, blotting out Chilton's farm, the straw stack, and the derelict cottage. He and Manfred climb aboard the army transport; faces freshly shaved, uniforms pressed, kit-bags packed. Hobart's aufwiedersehen! It is in this place that he has first encountered England. Who ever sees a country clearly from the wrong side of a barbed-wire fence? Here it is that they have set him free: opened the cage a crack, slipped the leash. He has no complaints. They are bound for Sheffield, he and Manfred Weiss, for the final processing before re-patriation.

Re-patriation; it is an emotive word in English or in German. He has talked it over with her in the intervals between the loving. If she had begged him, in that moment, to remain in England, he would have weakened; but she is an inexperienced girl, a green stranger to games of that sort; still unaware of the power women wield at such times.

'You must decide,' she has told him, 'I will live with you in your country, if that is what you want.'

There are back rooms in his mind, with doors he has slammed shut years ago. His father is dead, slaughtered with a million others before Stalingrad. That door is bolted fast. His mother and sister lurk behind looser shutters. When the letters come from the Soviet Zone he is forced to acknowledge the unimaginable hardships of their lives under Russian rule. He has not yet found an acceptable way of telling them that he has married in England.

*

'Where were you born?' The collecting-camp in Sheffield is stiff with British officers, all asking damn-fool questions. What can any of it matter now? This one is drumming his fingers on the desk, impatient to get the blasted form filled in before the orderly brings in his tea and biscuits.

'Pommern, East Germany – Sir.' So what?

The officer looks at his dossier again, but with more attention this time. 'Says here you have an English wife. How did you manage that, by God? Oh well, never mind. I suppose you know the risk you are running if you return to the Soviet Zone?'

'What risk – Sir? I was not a Nazi.'

'There's a rumour that the Russians are sending the fit young Germans to work in Russia, as soon as they return from prison camp; you could find yourself in a cattle truck bound for Siberia or the Ukraine. As for your English wife – they will never grant her a visa to enter their zone. Obstruction is their favourite pastime. If you must return, then take my advice and go to the British Sector. Have you any relatives there?'

He needs time to think it over, but the Englishman is waiting, pen poised impatiently for his answer. 'I have an aunt who is living near Hanover: she wrote me a letter. I could go there: see how is the life in the West.'

'A wise decision, Baumann. Keep away from the Russians. They're everybody's enemy.'

In company with Manfred Weiss and two thousand other prisoners-of-war he boards a British troopship three days later. The weather is as cold and depressing as it had been on the day of their arrival.

*

The music wakes him. Somewhere below decks someone is playing a mouth organ. The sad, sweet melody of 'Lili Marlene' comes drifting up like smoke from an open hatchway, to sting his eyes. He tries to close his ears against the sound. It reminds him of girls he has known; of camps and naval barracks; of things he has forgotten and considered lost. There will come a time, he knows, when certain memories will have to be dealt with, and assimilated into the man he has since become. But not yet. It is too soon: and he lacks the courage.

Halfway between sleep and consciousness, he sits firmly wedged into a quiet corner of the boat-deck. He could not have borne to go below, on this, of all nights, with the German coastline rolling closer with every turn of the screws. The wind is blowing directly from the east. It stings his face with the fierce caress he remembers from childhood: a snow-wind, straight off the steppes of Russia. Above his head the raw February twilight merges, and deepens in a sky of ebony in which stars glitter like ice chips. He needs this night-watch; it is the vigil he never kept for his dead father. Cathy already seems more distant than is warranted by the few hundred miles that lie between them. The English wolds, and that fold in the hills that shelters Hobart's farm has retreated to some far place in his memory. He is experiencing a subtle sea-change: shuttling back and forth between past and future, in the land-locked tides of remembrance.

He goes below, clumsy with cold, slipping a little on the greasy gangways, and stamping the pins-and-needles out of his feet. After half an hour the stench of close-packed bodies and vomit drive him back to the boat-deck.

Manfred comes up to join him towards the morning. He looks queasy; he is clutching a mug of hot tea, but not drinking.

'What's it like down below?'

'Like a bloody mortuary. Most of them are vomiting, and they're depressed enough to jump in the sea. It was bad enough when they caught us in '44; going back is a damn sight harder.' Manfred huddles deeper into his overcoat. 'Two thousand of us on board, and it feels like a ghost ship. Lousy English crew. The poor sods were torpedoed in '43, so they say, and it's certainly soured their dispositions. You did better to say up here.'

Manfred has never been so forthcoming. In the four years of their acquaintanceship this man has scarcely volunteered an opinion on the weather. He shivers violently, and is off again. 'One of the crewmen said that he is sick of playing ferryman to a bunch of Jerries, and if it was up to him he would tip the lot of us to the fishes.'

Kurt laughs: 'What did you say to that?'

'"Go on then you bastard," I tell him, "See if I care."'

Kurt tries to get a glimpse of the other man's face, but between the pulled down peak of the cap and the upturned coat collar there is nothing much to be seen. The voice is revealing. 'I got a letter just before we left Hobart's. From my wife. I've never had many from her, but this was a beauty. Trying to set the record straight before I get back and hear all about it from the neighbours.'

'Oh,' said Kurt, 'one of those.'

'Exactly. She's been living with an American: a coal-black sergeant. She says that the children were starving and this was her only chance of getting food for them.'

Kurt is no counsellor but he is ready to concede that during the war, female fidelity might also have had its areas of greyness. 'Judge not, that ye be not judged,' he quotes uncomfortably to Manfred, who ignores him, and walks a little unsteadily towards the ship's rail. Suddenly, Manfred lifts the mug of tea shoulder high, and hurls it overboard into the North Sea.

A passing crewman stops to remonstrate with him, 'If you don't like our tea old mate, there's no call to throw it in the sea, mug and all.'

In any other place, at any other time, they might have laughed.

*

A thick white mist hangs above the sea: the ship seems hardly to be moving. He paces the deck in an attempt to restore his circulation; he has always detested the hours he had been forced to spend cooped up below deck: now he can begin to taste the freedom on his tongue, and he will savour it. The troopship enters the mouth of the Elbe at three o'clock in the afternoon; they are coming in on a strong tide. At last they are in German waters, and their officers, who have held themselves aloof from the men throughout the voyage from England, finally condescend to join the rank and file on the decks. The officers had been allowed to retain their German uniforms, and now they stand about, garbed in shabby glory, like homecoming tourists who have overstayed their leave, and are slightly uncertain of their welcome. 'Look at the swine,' Kurt mutters to Manfred, 'already they've washed their hands of us. I wonder what their excuses will be when they get home.'

The vessel, looking more than ever like a funeral ship, moves slowly up river towards the ruined port of Hamburg. Dark grey waters lap at grey ship's hull under a sky of iron, while white-faced men continue to come on deck, until they are standing several hundreds deep at the ship's rails.

It is not to be the homecoming they have envisaged in the long years of their captivity. This is reality, stark and inescapable.

There is to be no cheering: no back-slapping cameraderie. Only this aching progression towards a port they hardly recognise as their old Hansastadt. It is an hour that lasts longer than most, and yet, as he steps onto German soil his flesh aches with the poignant pleasure of this homecoming. All memory of the long captivity in England is obliterated in that instant. He is a German, and he has come home.

They are numbered, documented, processed, and finally released three days later. The demobilisation camp in Münster has provided the minimum requirements for re-entry into civilian life; but the only item of value to Kurt Paul Baumann is that scrap of paper that confirms him as a civilian – now, and for all time.

*

Mild English winters have made him forget how bitter is the winter cold in his country. The land is gripped in a fist of frost: rivers and lakes are frozen bank to bank, and snow still lies from a recent, heavy fall. He has been on the move for almost a week, and he is weary. Only elation at this new freedom to go where he pleases keeps him moving towards the Weserbergland and Dietkirchendorf. The final stage of his journey will have to be made on the 'kleinbahn', a shabby little train which runs on narrow gauge track, and links together the villages of the region. The mountain air seeps under the doors and in at the windows making him shiver in spite of the Yorkshire wool and Bradford cloth of his prisoner's uniform. He is travelling now in the state of Lower Saxony, in that strange and secretive hill-country that lies beyond Hanover. The landscape looks unreal in the cloudy yellow light of afternoon. From the train he looks out on craggy hillsides that are dark with overhangs of rock, and narrow passes full of rushing water. Foreign armies have come this way, and not so long ago: rolling up against these ancient rocks, but leaving no sign of their passing. The land is proud, as it has always been: only the people submit.

He remembers England. Hobart's farm last spring, and the meadow grass emerald and springy under his feet. Primroses in the hedgerows. The British are the only nation he knows who have allowed themselves the self-indulgence of hedges: full of nesting birds and wild flowers. No German had ever layered the hawthorn until he came to England.

The train is tilted upwards, grinding its inevitable way towards Dietkirchendorf and his Tante Emma. What is he doing here anyway? But for the interference of that officer in Sheffield he would, by this time, have been sitting in a train bound for Berlin, and that much closer to Pommern.

He wonders if the Stettiner Bahnhof still stands in Berlin. It had always been the railway station he knew best: the first place he had made for when the Navy gave him leave. Once, in the spring of 1942, he had bought great bunches of white and blue lilac from the flower-seller who sat at the station entrance. He had carried the blossom home to his mother, who had two lilac trees in her garden anyway. A man is watching him from the opposite seat. An old man who wears a stained American forage cap and a threadbare overcoat. His face is seamed and pocked with the bluish scars of old powder-burns and his blue eyes water incessantly; he gazes expectantly at the flat tobacco tin that holds the English cigarettes.

Kurt offers the tin, and then grows alarmed as the old man draws the smoke deep into his lungs, and then almost chokes to death from the unexpected pleasure.

'Du lieber! the English cigarettes are strong,' he gasps. 'You just came back from prison camp?'

'A few days ago.'

'You look healthy. It's lucky that the British caught you. You should see the boys who are coming back from Russia: they look older than I do.' He coughs dryly. 'They only release them when they're dying, you know: when they can't work any more. You come from these parts boy?'

'I am from Pommern. My aunt and cousins are living in a place called Dietkirchendorf, I am going there to talk to them; to get some idea of what's been happening lately.'

The man takes a wary pull on his cigarette, 'I'm from Dietkirchendorf. What's her name then, this aunt of yours?'

'Becher. Emma Becher.'

'Never heard of her. But then, the village is full of refugees these days. She'll be somewhere among them, if she's from the East.' Remembering the gift of the cigarette, he adds, 'Poor devils!'

It has never occurred to Kurt Baumann that he too might be classed as a refugee. From what, or whom, will he be seeking refuge? This is still Germany, in spite of foreign occupation. Surely to God they are still one people?'

'These refugees,' he asks urgently, 'are they all Germans?'

The answer is laconic. 'A mixture I reckon. They come from Pommern, Silesia, Danzig, Latvia, Poland: and anywhere else you like to mention east of the Oder-Neisse line. Where the hell have you been boy? Don't you know anything? We're in a proper mess in Germany, I can tell you. You work your guts out for a few pfennigs. You buy or barter – black market; your house, or what's left of it, is commandeered and stuffed full of bloody refugees.' He leans forward, and looks closely into Kurt's eyes. 'Tell me: is it true what they say? That you could have stayed behind in England? You must be out of your mind to come back to this place.'

'How do they live – these refugees?' Kurt asks him; ignoring the old man's question.

'Oh – they all have to go to work for Heldmann, up at the Kalkwerk.'

'Kalkwerk?'

The old man sighs and gestures towards the hills. 'That stuff up there is limestone, sonny. Dietkirchendorf is built on it, see. We blast it out and then bring it down to the plant, for smelting. We had French POWs working in the quarries all through the war. Now we have refugees. It's a lousy job, but they're glad enough to be here.'

He rubs his face and looks resentfully at Kurt.

'Not many young ones came back from the war. I had four boys. Lost them all in Russia. Only poor old sods like me are left to blast out the stone, these days.'

Kurt shifts uneasily in his seat. 'Where do the refugees live?'

'There's a hostel, just beyond the village. It's falling down, derelict really, but beggars can't be choosers. The single men live there, married men get a room in the village. Four or five families have to share a house. It makes for plenty of trouble: it's the refugees you see; nobody wants them.'

He pauses and looks hopefully at the tobacco tin. 'There's a widow,' he says helpfully, 'who lives in an attic above the factory office. Could well be she's the aunt you're looking for.'

*

He sees it for the first time from the train: the village called Dietkirchendorf. It rises like a natural growth from the menacing limestone mountain: looking exactly like an illustration he had once seen in a book of fairy-tales. Was it the Brothers Grimm? he can't remember. Cathy will know. He grins involuntarily, as he steps down from the train. It is the kind of unimportant detail that a girl like her will have at her fingertips.

He finds the factory almost at once, behind a faded sign which reads 'Heldmann und Pieper. Kalkwerk.' The lying snow has merged with the fine white limestone dust which covers the sprawl of ancient buildings. High above the factory office a single light bulb burns in an attic window. He opens a door and calls out, but there is no reply. Hunching his shoulders within the narrow stairway, and thrusting kitbag and suitcase before him, he climbs the stairs. There had been no time to warn her of his arrival, but she recognises him straight away. She had been young and pretty once, his Tante Emma: now she wears black, and the plaits of dull gold hair look too heavy for the thin stem of her neck to carry comfortably. She looks defeated; a woman with a burden, and no place where she may safely set it down. She begins to apologise for the smallness of the attic room. But they are lucky to have this degree of privacy: others are not so fortunate. Annaliese, once his baby cousin, and now a leggy ten-year-old, kisses him shyly. Bruno, grown incredibly tall in a French prison camp, claps his shoulder repeatedly: cannot stop talking. They crowd around, pulling off his overcoat, and sitting him down by the stove. Tante Emma fetches him bread and sausage, and a steaming mug of kaffee-ersatz.

Tears sting his eyelids: and for several minutes he is unable to speak, he can feel the muscles in his face relaxing, and the peace flowing through him. He savours the sour, almost forgotten taste of the dark rye bread, and the bitter residue which the kaffee-ersatz has left on his tongue.

These dear people are his family, bound by blood and language, by memories shared, the good and bad.

The hand that bears the English wedding ring is thrust deep inside his jacket pocket. It is, after all, the mark of his betrayal.

*

Bruno is full of the words that have been tamped down, and considerately withheld from his grieving mother; but Kurt has heard it all before, in prison huts, when the days were long and hope was non-existent. These old questions, of whom and what they should blame for defeat: and how did they manage to get it all so wrong, are all superfluous now. He will be done with all that: blot it out.

He turns back to his aunt. 'So what happened to you Tante?'

'The Russians came into Pommern.' On her lips the words sound more like a curse than a statement. 'Annaliese and I, got away across the Danish border. A few months ago they set us free, and sent us to this place. I have a job of sorts. I cook for the single men in the hostel. It means a roof above our heads, and one good meal a day.'

'But Tante – why come here to Saxony – why not Pommern?'

Bruno says: 'Mensch! don't you know what has happened? Pommern is Polish Territory now. Haven't you heard of the Potsdam agreement? What were you doing in England – dreaming? They carved us up pretty neatly those three bastards, Churchill, Roosevelt and Stalin. They sliced us up like a wedding cake. Pommern's gone. Forever. Like it never existed. Wiped off the map of Europe. Some bloody, rapist Polaks are strutting about in Mechtenhausen these days. We shall never see home again.'

Tante Emma says, 'Bruno: that sort of talk does not become you. It has happened. That is all. Leave it.' She fingers the dark stuff of her dress. 'You know that our Papa is fallen in Russia?'

Kurt looks grim. 'Yes. My mother wrote me.'

'Your dear father too, Kurt. My husband and my brother, both lie dead in that terrible country.'

Surreptitiously, he slips the gold band from his finger: and still concealing it inside his jacket, he eases it quietly into the empty tobacco tin.

*

His purpose had been to reconnoitre: to talk things over. But the hunger and devastation in his country are on a scale he had never dreamed possible, when he courted a girl, and married her in England. A man would need to be untrammelled in such a situation, if he was to do what was right and proper by his family; but a wife, and an Englander at that, must now be included in any plans he might want to make. He knows that he has completely misjudged the whole situation. Quite suddenly he is caught up in rules and regulations; there are matters requiring immediate attention, all of them containing a disturbing threat of permanence. The attic room is so tiny it barely suffices for his Aunt and Annaliese: Bruno sleeps each night in the refugee hostel. But if Kurt Baumann wishes to secure this same security he will be forced to sign on for work in Heldmann's quarry; and before he makes any move at all he must register with the police. He finds that as a civilian he will need ration cards and clothing vouchers. Within the hour his pockets are crammed with permits. Identity papers: insurance cards: permission to work, to walk the street, to breathe. The freedom on which his future plans are based is proving to be illusory. The full weight of the new-style German bureaucracy is falling upon him (it is not so different from the old one) and it is proving to be more constricting than anything he had experienced in the prison camps of England.

He had seen himself as a transient in this mountain community, on his way to somewhere better. But there is, it seems, no place that is going to be any better than this one. Germany is down on its luck, and he is on his knees with the rest of them: grovelling for ha'pennies.

*

The hostel is a depressing facsimile of every camp and barracks he has ever lived in. Cold and bare; the smells of unwashed men and dirty blankets mingle with damp and the rank odour of mice. Food is sent up to the quarry at midday; watery soup and a slice of dry bread is the ration for refugees who work: God knows what happens to the others. In the evenings they all sit down to the same inadequate fare. On Sundays the bowl of soup is flanked by a miniscule portion of cheese or sausage. The native villagers, he sees, have a few hens or even a pig to supplement their starvation diet. Refugees have nothing. Refugees break stone: and stone, he soon learns, does not turn into bread.

At first he sets off for work in total darkness: falling in line behind the long column of men who make the daily climb up to the quarries. He dreads that early morning walk along the mountain road. The blackness underneath the overhang is deep and full of menace: it re-awakens old, primitive fears he thought he had left behind with his childhood. It has taken so little of hunger and disillusion to erode his courage. He must have grown soft in England. But then, as each successive morning becomes a little lighter, the pricking in his thumbs diminishes. At first it is only a light green haze that shrouds the tips of the limestone hills: a pale, apple-tinted promise of the returning spring. But by midday he finds a softness in the air, and an infinity of blue sky curving away from the grey walls of the quarry. Later on there is birdsong, which he loves, and tiny clumps of violets growing on shady banks at the forest's edge. By evening it will be cold again: but he knows now that the springtime lies waiting; coiled beneath the dark grey mountain. Just as it always has been.

*

The English wedding ring rattles around in the empty tobacco tin with every movement that he makes. He thinks it sounds like a reproach that is determined to be heard. He is surprised that Bruno has not made some comment.

The hostel is quiet: most men are outdoors on that fine April morning. Kurt Baumann reserves his Sunday mornings for chores and letter-writing. A refugee, more than most, should observe discipline, and a certain degree of order in his doings. He shakes up the straw in the canvas bag that serves him as a mattress, and looks across the room at his cousin Bruno.

Bruno is deep in the ritual of his Sunday morning shave; squinting sideways into the precious sliver of mirror which isn't big enough to reflect all his face at once. Kurt folds his blankets neatly, lining up the edges, and placing the pillow four square on the top. He sweeps the floor; carefully clearing away the bits of straw that have filtered between the wide mesh of the canvas. The locker which holds his few possessions is so tidy it might be awaiting officer's inspection: but the state of his mind will not bear investigation. He begins to polish the real leather brogues he brought with him from England: shoes that are so valuable in Germany, that he can rarely bring himself to wear them.

'I got married when I was in England.' He tries to make it sound casual: an everyday occurrence.

Bruno eyes him cautiously through the scrap of mirror: and slowly wipes lather from his face. 'Stop kidding around,' he mutters. Kurt says, very quietly, because it has suddenly become a matter of urgency that he should be believed, 'I married an English girl: in a place called Kingsbridge, in the County of Rutland, on January 16th of this year.' He fumbles inside the tobacco tin, and as he pushes the wedding ring over his knuckle he sees that his hands are shaking.

Bruno stares for a long, unnerving moment: and then he begins to laugh: great gusts of laughter that billow around the room.

'You?' he roars. 'Old Casanova! you used to say that no girl would ever catch you.' The exquisite humour of the revelation sends Bruno staggering to his bed. 'So they took you prisoner so that some English girl could nail you to the mast.' Bruno lies spreadeagled, and laughing helplessly upon his thin, straw mattress: 'No, no, I don't believe it. Not you, mein lieber man; not you.'

Kurt opens his wallet (a parting gift from Cathy) and pulls out a piece of paper. 'Here, read it. It's my certificate of marriage.' The words sound strange in his ears: it is as if it is he, and not Bruno who needs convincing.

*

Tante Emma asks women's questions.

'Her name is Catherine,' Kurt tells her; stumbling as ever over the diphthong in the English name. 'She's nineteen years old and tiny. Comes up to my shoulder. Her hair is a sort of reddish colour, and her eyes are blue. She reads books, likes music.' He spreads his hands wide in a deprecating gesture. 'She's English, and their women are more,' he hunts for the word, 'more – outspoken. But there are compensations. She's delicate – you know, thin-boned, soft-skinned: but she is doing a man's job and not complaining. This was the first thing I noticed about her,' he grins, and lowers his left eyelid, 'well, one of the first things, anyway.'

Bruno sees some kind of Nemesis in the fact that Kurt has been joined with the enemy's daughter, while in their camp, and still their prisoner. Tante Emma is kinder. 'Go down to the Housing Amt at once,' she urges, 'get your name on the list. You will need a room in the village for when your wife comes.'

He is informed by a brisk official that a room in the dentist's house on Lahweg Strasse will be coming vacant on the 1st of May. 'But' he is told, 'your wife must be resident in Dietkirchendorf by that date. Such accommodation cannot be given to a single man.'

He strolls along Lahweg Strasse in the cool spring evenings, passing and re-passing the dentist's greystone dwelling. Dusk hides the shabbiness of the house, and the ravages that foreign armies have wrought in the village. Already he feels proprietorial pride: he wonders which of the lighted windows will be his on the 1st of May. He writes straight away to England, phrasing his ultimatum in the plainest possible German. 'I have been promised a room on May 1st but you must be living here on that date, or I shall lose it.' She writes back: in English. 'The Foreign Office don't seem very keen to grant me a visa. I write every week, but they never answer. Our newspapers say that the Germans are starving: that Berlin is completely cut off, and that food is being airlifted in. What are the Russians up to? Don't you think it would be wiser if you tried to get back to England? I miss you: I have no courage since you went away.'

He sends her long letters of reassurance. 'I will stand by you: work hard for you, I will do all that you can ever expect me to. It will not be easy: you are not used to hardship on such a scale, but we will overcome difficulties together. Germany cannot possibly remain in this mess forever. It will be a good place to live in, and bring up our children: I know it. Only trust in me, and come quickly. I will always be a loving husband to you. I will not fail you.'

Her reply is cool, and full of prevarication. She does not seem to have comprehended a single word he has written.

On the 1st of May the key of the room in the dentist's house is handed to a young couple who are expecting their first baby.

*

The loss of the room is a bitter blow. He has already bartered the cigarettes and chocolate Cathy sends him, for a wardrobe, a table, a couple of chairs. Possession of this single room was to have been his first step; it would not make of him the solid burgher of his dreams: but at this crisis in his life any move forward, he thinks, must have some significance for him.

Pain does not go away by itself, and he knows his own limits: his inability to dissimulate, to rationalise, to accept what life offers, or hammers him with. There is a sourness in his throat: a rawness in his chest. For the first time in his life he is sick of his own company.

*

As soon as he enters the Gasthof he sees her standing behind the bar: but since he never drinks anything alcoholic he is able, at first, to avoid her. He stands at the edge of the floor and watches the dancers. Girls, of necessity, must partner each other; men are in short supply these days: they are mostly lying beneath the fields of France and Russia. A three-piece band is playing a waltz, and he is awash with nostalgia for Mechtenhausen and village dances: for cycling home at first light through the deep forest, already half-asleep, the music still rolling around in his head.

As if he has signalled to her, she stands before him: 'I am Hildegard,' she says, 'shall we dance?'

Barmaids have never been his weakness: why should this one be any different? She is tall, for a woman, wide hipped, broad breasted. He has known Silesian girls who had this same black hair and moist skin. As she grips his hand the gold band of her ring bites into his fingers. 'Where's your husband?'

'He's dead. Fallen in Russia.' Her face is blank. 'I'm one of the Fatherland's several thousand widows. Joke is of course that I never really had time to be a wife.' She moves closer, 'I haven't seen you in here before, and I would have noticed you, believe me!'

'I came back from England. A few months ago.' He is monosyllabic, his good manners, it seems, will extend only to good girls. She is looking at him with increased interest.

'I've heard about you. They say that you married an Engländerin while you were still a prisoner. That was a bit cheeky wasn't it?' He shrugs, and does not reply.

'So what have you done with her then? Why isn't she here with you?'

'I'll tell you,' he says through clenched teeth: 'she's in a pink bedroom with a doll and a teddy-bear and a hundred bloody books: and how does a normal man compete with that lot?'

Hildegarde moves even closer; she presses a magnificent leg between both of his: 'I've never had a teddy bear,' she whispers, 'come to think about it, I don't even read all that well.'

'Ach, shut up,' he mutters, 'and just keep dancing. I've had a gutful of women who talk.'

*

He is coming apart in some internal region that he has not, until now, even known that he owned. None of the past dilemmas of his twenty-six years can equal this one in its scope for disaster. Concentrated thought on the subject of human emotion has never seemed necessary or desirable to him; but now he is forced to indulge himself: and at great length.

The first mistake, of course, had been to fall in love: and not the usual kiss and run variety either: but the whole performance. The sort of thing his father had recommended to him when he first began to shave. A nice girl is what you look for, Papa had said, one you can respect. A quiet girl who goes to church on a Sunday: and who knows when to say no! Even his father though, already three years dead, lying in a frozen grave in Russia, could not have anticipated that such a girl would be found by his son in England, within the enemy's gates; or that he would feel himself so drawn to her, so drowned in love, that he could not escape, even though the English were about to hand him back his freedom anyway. His second mistake had been to expect her to live in his country. Oh, she promised him; biblically, Ruth standing already among the alien corn! 'Your people are my people. Wherever you go I will follow.' But how can he go back to England: it is not possible for him to jump on a train, a boat, arrive. He will need, as ever, permission from some ruling authority. He sneaks a day away from the quarry, and cycles thirty miles to Bad Salzuflen, to the headquarters of the British Military.

'You should have stayed in England,' he is told, 'you had the option. Any German POW who wished to, was allowed to remain. Since you already had an English wife I am amazed that you chose to return to Germany. You can fill in an application form: but these things take time.'

He hates the work in the quarry. The breaking of stone demoralises him: it smacks of slave labour, is the traditional punishment for convicted criminals. He came back to Germany expecting hardship: and if stones need to be broken he is prepared to do his share. But not for too long.

*

In June the maize stands high in the fields below the village: recalling Pommern and other summers. He lies on the slope of the hill, and looks down at the window of Hildegarde Siefert's room: and he thinks about the sin he has not yet allowed himself to commit. The Lutheran Pastor, thundering in the Mechtenhausen church, would have been able to put him right on that score. It was one of his favourite 'thou shalt not's'.

Hilde has written a letter: has slipped it into his pocket while they are dancing. It seems that she too has adultery on her mind. The latest missive from Grossbritannien is also heavy with promise. 'I shall come,' writes Cathy, 'as soon as my visa is ready.'

*

One week later he crosses the East German frontier illegally and in darkness. He boards a train for Dresden, and nobody questions his right to do so: he looks as poor and as hungry as everyone else. The Russians are everywhere: in the streets and shops, on the railway platform. His mother and sister live in two rooms: they draw the curtains and bolt the door on his arrival; his life and their safety depend on such measures; it is just like the old days, under Hitler. His sister has just been discharged from hospital, she is sick, both legs are heavily bandaged: the result she says, of malnutrition and certain 'hardships' suffered at Russian hands.

His mother, dear God! He can hardly bear to look at his mother. At the age of forty-eight she looks like a woman of eighty. He has never, in his most pessimistic moments, imagined that things are this bad. He has looked upon Dietkirchendorf as being the ultimate in deprivation. He has brought food, in a rucksack. For a week, at least, they will eat. They have certain information for him. Remember, they say: remember Valli. The one with the long brown legs and the flaxen hair. Well, the Russians caught her, or was it the Poles? She ran: a mistake, a woman should never run from them; too many men will follow the one who flees. They caught her: in a barn: about twenty of them. They locked the door. When we found her three hours later, she was dead. Oh well, they say; not daring to meet his eyes, but determined that he shall know it; it happened to all of us women, young and old, to some degree, or other. We could not escape it.

He can feel the vomit rise in his throat. The tide of hatred begins in his feet, and comes up to his brain, and swamps him: and he is impotent in the face of their anguish: the final humiliation. His father is dead. His mother shows him a tattered wallet, a few letters, the pipe his father once smoked. Souvenirs brought back from the front by a surviving comrade: they mean nothing to him. He has seen such things a thousand times before.

His sister's husband has been reported missing. Not dead, she emphasises, twisting the ring on her finger. 'We must wait in Dresden for Ernst,' says Christina, 'his mother and brothers are also here. This is the place he will come back to. Here, he will find us.' He shows them his trophies. The wedding-ring: the marriage certificate, Cathy's photo.

His certainties, his expectations, are suddenly made unreal. He will be haunted in the night by what he has learned in this flattened, obliterated city where only ghosts dwell. As they talk together across a rickety table, the June sunshine is hot beyond the closed curtain. But he thinks he will never feel warm again.

Part Three

1979

Jürgen Hecht had made no move to return to the compartment, and Cathy, unusually reluctant to be alone, had lingered on in the dining-car with him. Luncheon was served promptly at twelve as promised.

'I think it's supposed to be wiener schnitzel,' she grumbled, 'but it tastes more like cardboard: and the potatoes came out of a tin.' She pushed her plate to one side of the table. She had recognised the hills that were just coming into view.

'I can't normally eat much,' Jürgen confessed, 'but I seem to have found an appetite from somewhere.' He waved his fork at the window, 'We are running into the Weser valley now, there is a narrow pass in these hills, where the river comes hurtling through. It's quite a spectacular sight.'

'I've seen it,' she said, 'I know this part of Germany well. I lived on the other side of those hills in 1948.'

'That was not a good time for you to be here.'

'I knew what I was coming into; or at least, I thought so. At the age of nineteen I imagined that I could take on the world single handed – and win. I had promised my husband that I would live in his country.' She picked up a spoon and began to trace a nervous pattern with it. 'I also had a presentiment that something was wrong. His letters were cooler and less frequent. It seemed that he had lost the tenancy of a room, and somehow it was all my fault.' She slammed the spoon down hard on the table. 'Well, my visa was finally granted, and over I came, all starry-eyed and romantic. Dear God. The courage we find at the age of nineteen.' She smiled at the window, 'The first time I saw that landscape out there I thought I was in a fairytale by the Brothers Grimm. You know, captive princess, enchanted forests, ruined castles. I could not equate it with the Germany I had seen on the Movietone News. Where had the jackboots gone, and the uniformed thugs and the banners? And how did they ever gain credibility in the first place, in amongst all that beauty?'

Dietkirchendorf. July 1948

The telegram arrives on a Sunday morning in July. It is delivered by the youthful one-armed postman (only survivor from a sunken U-boat), whose pinned-up sleeve looks more than usually tragic as he hands over the latest word from England.

'Arriving Hanover. Monday. 2 p.m. Love. Cathy.'

*

Hanover station lost its roof in an early air-raid, the re-building has just begun in the summer of 1948. The electric storms in that area are spectacular, and a particularly bad one has hit the district that day. Forked lightning plays in and out of the new iron girders, and piles of new bricks steam gently in the humid air. Kurt Baumann searches for a red-haired girl; since the telegram came he has lived through this scene a hundred times. She will step down from the train straight into his arms: he will kiss her. 'We will never be parted again,' she will cry.

In the event, he is quite unable to find her.

He is wearing his English brogues, and the suit of emerald green serge that he had been given in the demobilisation camp, in Münster. In the murky light his yellow hair shines out like a lighthouse beacon. The train from the Hook van Holland pulled into the station ten minutes ago; he must have missed her. He walks once again to the very end of the platform, and then he spots her, sheltering from the rain at the side of a workman's hut.

She has the skinned and piteous look of a frightened rabbit. As he runs towards her he can hear the panic break in her voice. 'I thought I had been abandoned,' she wept, 'I thought you weren't coming.' He begins to speak, and finds that he cannot remember a single word of English: so he grips her shoulders too hard, and feels the delicate bones move under his fingers.

Her tears are turning to laughter. 'I saw you pacing up and down, but I didn't recognise you,' she spluttered. 'You look exactly like Robin Hood in that bright green outfit. I only remember you wearing prisoner's uniform, and you've lost so much weight –'

'Slowly, please,' he interrupts her, 'I forget much English, speak only German in last months.' He kisses her briefly. 'Come. We find train. Go up to Dietkirchendorf.'

*

The storm is receding northwards towards Lüneburg Heath and the mountains of the Harz. The blue bellied clouds sag over the rim of the limestone hills and already the air is fresher. A watery sun appears and Kurt takes this to be an omen.

They sit side by side on the crowded kleinbahn: his eyes start to ache from the effort of glancing sideways at her; she has adopted her good girl's stance, hands folded in lap, eyes downcast. It is a pose she is good at; but he has known her in other situations; can vouch for the woman beneath the starch. She is much prettier than he remembers: but she has that brittle look that he recalls as being peculiar to the red-haired English. He dredges up English words from the depths of six months separation. 'You have not wear summer dress before – I have not see this.'

She looks surprised. 'But it was winter Kurt when I met you. I never knew you in summertime.' And this, he thinks, is the problem stated. The hundred days of his courtship had never included the golden, easy days.

It is late in the afternoon when they reach the village. He takes her to Tante Emma's room: he has nowhere else to go. He cannot tell her, at once, that he is a refugee and therefore homeless. He offers her food but she shakes her head at the dark rye bread and greasy sausage. It is the whole of his ration for that week that he wishes to give her, but she does not yet appreciate these finer points of her situation.

'Where do they actually live then? your aunt and cousins.'

'Here,' he speaks roughly, 'this is the place: one room: one attic room. It is small, yes? But this is how people like us have to live in Germany now.' The edgy grin that twists his mouth does not conceal that his words are meant as an accusation. She begins to pick nervously at the stitching on the belt of her cotton dress.

'Why have we come to your aunt's room. Where do you live: and when are we going there?'

'I live in refugee hostel with one hundred other men. Tonight we must sleep in hotel. That will cost much money. Tomorrow? I do not know what happens. You should have been here in May: now it is all too late. We have no place to go.'

Her parents' house has six rooms and a bathroom. They live on the pleasanter side of town, and she has never had to share a bedroom. Hardship for her has been a missed meal, or making her winter coat last another season. He is trying hard, but he thinks he will never arrive at the point where she has always been; and all he had ever wanted was happiness, with her or without her.

*

Admission to the Military Zone of Germany is only permitted to people who hold a visa: and hers had been granted on July 2nd.

'I couldn't come sooner,' she insists, 'I thought you understood. I wrote: explaining.'

'But the room,' he repeats, 'the Housing Amt do not allow me to keep it, because you are not here.'

'Well you will have to apply again. Tell them your wife is here, and you must have somewhere to live.'

'I have already do this. Early this morning I go to office. My name is at bottom of list. Come back, they say, in one year. Maybe we have a place for you.'

She moves across to the window. 'I shouldn't have come here, should I? you don't really want me; perhaps you never did. I guessed there was something wrong. I could sense it in your letters.' He can hear a note of hysteria creep into her voice. 'How can I go back to England: what shall I say to them all? – well, I married a German and then found out that he didn't want me?'

Bleakly, he says, 'I have tell you all this in my letters. I have say to you, do not come yet: room is lost: no place to live.'

'But I don't understand your language,' she cries, 'I only took in the bits where you said you loved me: nothing else seemed important.' Her gesture embraces the attic room and the sour bread and unappetising sausage. 'How could I know it would be like this. Nobody told me.'

'That is not true,' he says coldly, 'I have tell you many times. Life is hard in my country, I say; not like in England.' He looks at her inefficient fingers: they would, he thinks, be more at home twanging violin strings. (She has admitted to having lessons.) Buckets and shovels repeatedly ripped the skin from her palms at Chilton's. He should have heeded the omens. 'I see black,' he says, 'I see only black for us in the future.'

She begins to cry with dedication: great shuddering sobs that alarm him; he had not intended to do such damage. 'Hey, hey! Immer den Kopf hoch – keep the chin up! Is not so bad, we manage OK together ja. There is one more attic room in this building. We sleep there for one, two nights: I have furniture stored there. Is not like hotel, but we have honeymoon still. We not have time to notice.'

She laughs, over-anxious he thinks for the consolation he has to offer. Laughter and tears come too easily from her: it makes him uneasy. He had not noticed in England that she was so childish. Some travel faster than others, he thinks and lately he has been running. If she wants to stay in the race with him, she has plenty of catching up to do.

During the years of his captivity the future had looked unpromising, but straightforward. He had intended to stamp the imprint of his foot on some portion of his Fatherland as soon as possible after his return. They owe him that much, he considers. Secretly, he has always wanted land: has coveted a few productive hectares east of the river Oder. The return to a defeated Germany might just be made more bearable, if he can have a piece of it to plough and call his own. But lately he had seen how firmly the Russians hold the eastern provinces: gripping so hard that the very soil is dying from the pressure. He knows there is no place for him there: and here in the West he is a refugee, despised by the local population: useful for breaking stone, and little else.

Civilian life is turning out to be full of unexpected pitfalls: his marriage is yet another complication; an uneasy alliance that closely touches his pride: always a tender spot with him. Cathy will not, he suspects, behave like a German wife: the signs are already visible. Seeing her so far from her own milieu, and floundering hopelessly in his, he is filled with apprehension. There is this business of the room. Privately, he suspects her of prevarication. Can it possibly have taken her six months to get a visa? The English never hurry, he knows this much from personal observation, but hell! If she had really wanted to come –

He talks things over with Bruno and Tante Emma.

'Rats,' they warn, 'there are rats in that attic room across the stairway.' He laughs, but it isn't funny at three o'clock in the morning, when Cathy screams and shakes him awake. 'A heavy weight,' she cries, 'on my feet, and two red eyes looking straight at me. It scampered off when I moved; but I know it was a rat.'

'You dream,' he assures her, 'no rat can live in this place: the people are near starvation.' He can see that she does not believe him. He feels shamed in her eyes; wrong footed again in a situation which is not of his making.

*

The plan is so simple that he should have thought of it for himself: but it has taken that bright boy Bruno to work out the details. 'If your wife is English, and the British are our masters, why not take full advantage of that fact. Surely they will be obliged to look after their own? Send Cathy to Hanover. Annaliese can go with her as guide. Let her speak to the British Commandant, ask for his help.'

Kurt sees this stratagem as being perfect, and deserving of appreciation, but all he receives from her is a blank refusal to co-operate. She accuses him, among other things, of being insensitive. 'I am shocked that you should even ask me to do such a thing. How can I marry a German, and then when the going gets tough, turn back to the British demanding assistance?'

'I see nothing wrong,' he says, 'in that: they are your people, why shall they not help you?'

A flush creeps under her pallor, and she cannot meet his eyes. 'Some people, old friends, have been quite nice about my marriage to you: but most of them were pretty awful to me.' Suddenly she is pleading, 'Don't make me do it please. I can't go to our army of occupation and cry "Look here – I married a German – now find me a place among all these ruins where I may live with him in comfort".' She pauses. 'There is something else. There are hundreds of homeless people in this village. How will they react if I jump the queue and get ahead of them because I'm English?'

He latches on to the only point in her argument which seems to him to have any relevance to the matter under discussion. 'This is Germany,' he rasps angrily, 'and we are not playing gentleman's game of cricket, or hunting foxes. Only the strong survive. I have learned that much from war. You will also fight, Cathy: and if being English is your only advantage, then by God, you will use it. I made you this order!' He does not intend to present her with an ultimatum: such arbitrary behaviour was never included in his plan for a perfect marriage. But neither does he propose to live with her in an attic, and share his bed with the village rats.

'You don't care then, that it makes me feel degraded to ask the British for help. I believe that we should take our chances along with the rest of the population.' He looks at her with contempt, and she falls silent. At last, he says, 'This marriage: it has started badly yes? It will not, I think, last very long. We have one chance only, but you will not do this one small thing for me. You are,' he searches for the word, 'you are unreliable. You make promises but you do not keep them.'

*

It is the accepted rule in any defeated country that the army of occupation will claim the structurally sound and most prestigious buildings for its own use. The British have hung out the flag on a fine old mansion in one of Hanover's most beautiful squares, which, in the circumstances then prevailing in that city, they have every right so to do.

Kurt Baumann hesitates before the pillared portico, unwilling at first to mount the shallow stone steps that lead up to the impressive entrance. He has accompanied Cathy under protest, and on her firm promise that he will not be required to open his mouth. But there had been, he reflects, no need to extract such an undertaking from her. On her own territory, she seems more than able to handle the situation.

Kurt has been reared in the German tradition which requires that respect be shown towards bureaucrats and minor officials. Faced by some petty clerk with a pen in his hand, and a sheaf of papers before him, he is promptly reduced to incoherence. Not so his English wife. She has already pointed out that these mandarins exist only for the purpose of complicating the otherwise simple affairs of ordinary people.

The desk is manned by a civilian clerk: a supercilious German girl, with piled up yellow hair and scarlet finger-nails. 'It will not be possible,' she trills, 'for you to see anyone here without an appointment.' Cathy raps smartly on the desk: for the first time he sees that his wife is also extremely short on patience. 'I am English,' she announces, 'therefore I don't need an appointment. I intend to sit in this hallway until somebody sees me Kindly convey that message to the soldier who runs this organisation.'

The girl is obliged to leave the desk unmanned: she is absent for some considerable time. A queue of harassed looking Germans is beginning to form behind them; Kürt can feel the sweat breaking out on his forehead. He looks apprehensively towards the sentries who flank the entrance. He remembers other military interviews in the not so distant past, in which craven obeisance had been demanded and given. Heels had been clicked in those days, and the right arm raised in salute. Old habits die hard; old fears even harder. He begins seriously to doubt the wisdom of Cathy's behaviour.

They are ushered into the presence of an officer whose name is Hampshire. A colonel no less! middle-aged and choleric of complexion, who invites them, politely, to be seated. Kurt finds himself coming to involuntary attention before an officer of this rank. He decides he will not sit down, but remains on his feet near the door. Cathy sits down and begins by explaining her unusual presence at such a time, in Lower Saxony. He hears a note of surprise creep into her voice, as if the ambiguity of her position is only now becoming quite clear to her. 'We have nowhere to live,' she finishes lamely, 'I was hoping that you might be able to help us.'

'I can make you no firm promise,' says the British colonel, 'housing is a matter of internal German policy, and quite beyond my jurisdiction. I can only ask, very politely, that consideration be given to your problem.'

Kurt looks around him. The officer's rosewood desk stands on a Turkey carpet; there are dark green sunblinds flapping at an open window, keeping this gentleman cool in Hanover's city heat. The spoils of victory are sweet and readily attainable. This man has his comforts. 'Are your living conditions so very bad then?' Even with the width of the room between them Kurt knows that the sympathy in the quiet English voice might prove to be her undoing. His discomfiture increases as she digs her fingernails into her palms and lowers her head. Her voice shakes slightly. 'We have a sort of attic place, underneath a roof, a storeroom really, not intended for human habitation. There is nowhere for me to do any cooking – always supposing that I had anything to cook, that is. At night the rats re-possess the attic: they run about on the rafters. Sometimes they come down and sit on the end of the bed.'

It sounds so much worse as she describes it. He wants to shout 'It's not my fault' but remembers his vow of silence just in time. The colonel glances briefly in his direction. 'Does your husband speak any English?'

'Hardly any,' she lies protectively.

At once the man's tone becomes conspiratorial, 'Look here my dear,' he begins, 'you are in an intolerable situation. I assume that you have parents?' She nods. 'Then why don't you go back to them: return to England and think the whole thing over?' His eyes rake her slender waistline and flat stomach: 'There seems to be no obvious reason for you to stay on here. We all make mistakes – perhaps you can make a fresh start.' He picks up a heavy bronze paperweight and sets it down quite sharply, 'I have a daughter at home who is just about your age –' But Cathy does not allow him to finish. Kurt can only see her profile, skin white as alabaster now, with the red hair unfurled above it like a flag of battle.

'You do realise,' she interrupts, 'that you have just advised me to leave my husband? You wouldn't have dared to treat him with such contempt if he were English. How can you judge that my marriage has been a mistake? It's a complicated story, but it comes down to this: all our present difficulties are entirely my fault. He has done his best in a difficult situation. He is not to blame in any way.'

The colonel's expression is frankly disbelieving. He leans back in his chair and says nothing. The silence only succeeds in goading her further and now she loses her temper completely. She slams both hands down hard on the desk. 'Oh I know what you're thinking,' she shouts, 'you believe that anyone who is stupid enough to marry a German must expect to take the consequences. The world is full of bigots like you. It's exactly the same for him you know! His people won't do us any favours either. They also look for loopholes. We seem to have broken some unwritten law by marrying one another. "Putting ourselves beyond the pale," I think it's called.'

Kurt sees her lean across the desk, her face just an inch from that of the astonished colonel. 'Well, I don't intend to leave him, and opposition from people like you only makes me the more determined to stay here. You can go to hell, and I'm sorry I ever asked for your help.'

The exchange has been too rapid for Kurt's complete understanding: but he has clearly heard her tell a high-ranking officer of the British Army to go to hell. He closes his eyes and wonders weakly what form her punishment is likely to take.

But this colonel is laughing. Great belly-laughs that shake his whole frame. 'By God,' he roars, 'I like your style: you've got guts. I only hope that German chappie appreciates his good fortune. Where do you say this village is?' He begins to make notes on his blotter. 'I'll be over to see you tomorrow. Bang on a few doors: kick up a bit of a shindig, what?'

They travel back to the village in silence: there is nothing left to say. He knows that in some subtle fashion the balance has shifted. In her favour.

*

The visit of a British officer to Dietkirchendorf is a singular event that is bound to cause comment among the population. His long black requisitioned Mercedes roars down the main street on a Friday morning: lurching among the dips and potholes, raising a cloud of dense white dust, and stampeding a passing team of yoked oxen. He inspects the stuffy attic above Heldmann's factory office: and spends ten diplomatic minutes in conversation with the Housing Amt making his wishes known. Then he departs. Within the hour, news of his visit and its purpose has spread throughout the length and breadth of the village. Baumann, Kurt. English-born wife Catherine, née Wyatt. Officially and unofficially homeless. Of no fixed or respectable abode. Suddenly they are commanding the attention of important people. Even Herr Hermann Heldmann, the owner of the Kalkwerk, develops a belated interest in one of his refugee workers as soon as a British colonel comes out on a welfare mission. The village is loud with whispers, it is rumoured that the Housing Amt (whose officials stand only one step lower than God) is incensed at the nerve of this Engländerin who has shown a typical, only to be expected, sneakiness, in running off to the British, and getting an official German edict overruled. But they are all agreed that it will be unwise to antagonise the Military at this stage. Who knows what favours they may themselves require in the future.

The Herr Administrator of Dietkirchendorf's Housing Amt will have no further dealings with Kurt Baumann. He orders that Cathy shall attend his office, alone, on the following Monday morning. When she appears before him head high, and determinedly unrepentant, he delivers a long and admonitory speech in German of which she understands perhaps half-a-dozen words.

The key that he gives her is labelled POLIZEI AMT, Hauptstr. 21. 'But surely Kurt, nobody actually lives in the Police Station; it must be a joke.' She shows Kurt the heavy eight-inch key made of filigreed iron. 'It's insulting that they should even think of housing us in the local lock-up. They have iron bars on all the windows. They've done this on purpose you know: to humiliate us. There must be some rooms to spare in normal houses.'

'We dare not refuse,' he says nervously, 'we have to take what we are given.' He holds up the key, 'This is an order from the Housing Amt: take it or leave it.'

They go at once to the tall grey building which houses the local police force, and climb the long flight of stairs that lead up to the second floor. Kurt turns the key in the lock, and the door swings open. He knows straight away that this elegant room could not have been found in the dentist's house on Lahweg Strasse.

Four long windows look down on Dietkirchendorf's main street. The ceiling is high and covered with plaster roses. The floor is of gleaming parquet; a blue and white cooking stove stands in one corner, and a huge pine dresser occupies one whole wall. He begins to prowl. He tests the windows, peers into the stove, and opens the dresser drawers. She remains rooted uncertainly beside the door. 'Do you think we have the right room?'

'The key fits,' he points out; 'your army friend has been good to you ja? They would never have given such a room to me.'

'It's like a ballroom,' she says, 'I think the policemen held dances up here in the old days.' Her voice grows dreamy, 'It needs chandeliers, and gilt-framed mirrors, and Chinese rugs.'

'Come here,' he says shortly, 'and look at the stove. You will use this for your cooking: it burns wood. I shall need to find a supply of logs and a place to store them.'

She crosses to where he stands, and looks down at the little blue stove with contempt. 'I can't use that thing. I only know how to cook with gas; and not very well at that.'

'My mother has always cooked with such a stove,' he says sternly, 'you must learn these things. You are a German wife now.'

*

They move in that same evening. Bruno helps to carry their few possessions: an iron bedstead with straw-filled mattress, a wardrobe, a flimsy table and two bentwood chairs. Tante Emma donates a chipped enamel bowl and a few pots and pans. He 'borrows' the two grey blankets that were refugee-hostel issue.

'No matter which way we arrange it,' moans Cathy, 'this room still looks empty.'

'I bartered all the good cigarettes you sent from England,' he tells her, 'to get these few things. You must understand that as a refugee I start with nothing.' He looks around him, 'but where is the trunk that you had sent out from England. We have room to unpack it now – give me the key.'

She hands over the key reluctantly. He thinks she looks frightened. When he throws back the lid of the trunk he knows why. The books have been carefully packed in neat layers. He lifts them out one by one. Slim volumes of verse bound in suede and leather: Milton, John Keats, Robert Browning. Who the hell are they?

'Where are the household things I told you to bring from your country?' His voice is too quiet.

'There's a brush and dustpan in there.' She sounds defensive, 'and a frying-pan and two egg-cups. I think.'

'Is that all?'

'My clothes. I need my summer dresses.'

'And your winter things – where are they? It will be cold in these hills by September. What will you do then?'

'I didn't expect to be here quite so long,' she says slowly.

He feels stunned. 'Then why did you come in the first place?' He can hardly believe it. 'You did not mean to keep promise to live in my country. You lied.'

Her shoulders twitch as if he has struck her, but she will not turn around to face him. 'I don't know Kurt. I don't know what I meant: it all happened so quickly. Nothing has turned out the way I expected.'

'So what did you hope to find in my country ha! Good house! six rooms! soft armchairs? It was your armies, your bombers who smash us: your parents' house was not damaged. You have not seen war in England.'

'There was the blitz,' she fights back, 'there was London and Coventry.'

'And I have seen Dresden,' he roars, 'I have seen Berlin and Hamburg. All is destroyed there, I have made visit to the East: I hear terrible things from my mother and sister. My people are starving and you bring me books from your land of plenty. Du lieber Gott.'

He sits down at the table and drops his head in his hands. 'We have no cups, no plates, no knives and forks. Do you know what that means? I must go to my aunt who is poorer than I am and beg for one cup, one plate, one knife. I have said in my letters – bring soap, bring coffee, with these I can barter. You have shamed me. You have brought books.'

She makes a tentative move towards him. 'There should be a few tablets of soap and some coffee in there somewhere: and I brought you some razor blades in my handbag.' He rises and plucks a small tin of coffee from the coloured tangle of her cotton dresses.

'I will go to the Schwarzmarkthendler,' he says heavily, 'perhaps I can make a bargain.'

*

The fugitive days and nights spent in Heldmann's attic have at least been carefree. Now they are key-holders: responsible people, they will need to handle their ration cards and their money wisely; and it seems that in this, as in most other ways, she will fail him. Nothing that she attempts is ever quite right. Her polished parquet looks greasy; she burns the precious potatoes; the ring of scum in the washing-up bowl, unnoticed by her, revolts him. She repeatedly irons the unwanted creases back into his shirts with a heavy hand. She is only adept at doing nothing: and doing it with such skill and panache that she gives an impression of working. This trick annoys him. He would prefer it if she was frankly indolent: sluttishly, lollingly lazy. But there is always the book in her hand, the pen and the paper. She scribbles in little green notebooks, and spends hours at the open window. Observing, she calls it. 'Observing what?' he wants to know.

'This village frightens me,' she tells him, 'it's still back in the Middle Ages. I believe they burn witches down there, in secret. Have you ever been into the forest, or felt the evil out on that mountain road? This was the land of the Brothers Grimm – this Weser Valley. It's Pied Piper country. Think of that Kurt! The whole place is bewitched; look! Even the houses grow crooked.'

Such talk makes him feel uneasy: he thinks she is slightly

unhinged. He brings her attention back to the curtainless windows. 'It is not respectable that we live so: we must have curtains.'

She laughs. 'Why bother. We are two floors up, who can see us?' She ruffles the hair at the nape of his neck 'Were you ever young, my dear old man? You make such a fuss about nothing.'

'Men of my age have had no time to be young,' he reminds her.

*

On Sunday he borrows a bike and cycles the fifteen miles to Hemmenstein. He has heard a rumour that in that village a black marketeer has put up some unbleached linen for barter. The heat is oppressive, and the Hemmenstein road full of flints and potholes. In a rucksack he carries the last of the perfumed soap and coffee; but the schwarzman is tough, and Kurt is obliged to throw in a packet of razor blades as well, before an exchange can be made.

'Now you will make us some curtains,' he orders Cathy, 'I have done my part.'

She fingers the linen reluctantly. 'I have to tell you,' she says, 'that I stab my fingers when sewing on buttons. I can't make curtains. I don't know how to.'

He is tired. He has made a round trip of thirty miles that day, on a rusty bike; he is in no mood for her lack of co-operation. 'Sit down,' he says, his voice like a whiplash, 'sit down and listen. I could make the curtains for you, ja. I learned to sew in the Navy. But you are the wife: I expect you to do the sewing now, it is the woman's place. In Germany, a girl learns how to cook and sew before she gets married.'

Cathy rounds upon him, face blazing. 'Then you should have married a German girl, shouldn't you. One of your own kind: a drudge, always scrubbing and cleaning and finding fault. Oh what a happy couple you would have made.' She grabs at the bolt of linen, and using it as a battering ram, she runs at him with it. 'Get out of here and don't come back in until I have finished. I'll make your bloody curtains for you, but not while you watch me. Do you know what our trouble is Kurt? I'll tell you. I get everything wrong because you make me so bloody nervous. You are so bloody good at everything, aren't you?'

He calculates that she has said bloody at least three times; he doesn't approve of women who swear, but it hasn't seemed quite the right moment to tell her so. He picks up the empty rucksack and makes for the door. He says stiffly that he must return the borrowed bike to its owner. She doesn't answer: she has already begun to measure one of the four long windows with an old bit of fraying string.

*

Out on the street he finds that the air is warm, and filled with the scents and sounds of a summer's evening. It is Saturday night and down at the Gasthof the three-piece band is playing a waltz. The music comes drifting out to where he is standing under the churchyard yew trees: and he finds himself thinking of Hildegarde Siefert. He restores the bike to its owner, and walks smartly away from the village, and out to the Kalkwerk.

The refugee kitchen is newly-built, but already looks shabby. He often wonders why this should be. It upsets him: and offends his sense of the fitness of things. New is new: should, for some time at least, remain pristine and perfect. Perhaps it is due to the fact that the joiners are forced into using unseasoned timber. There is no time to wait for wood to mature in Germany these days: and no paint to be had with which to preserve it. Build up, restore, refurbish. It is all that is left for them to do. But how; and with what? The results are not always what people had meant when they started. Tante Emma is still in the kitchen. She stands at the stove, cooking porridge. Thin soup at midday, and porridge for supper, the diet can never be varied. A small cube of meat or cheese on Sundays: potatoes, if you are lucky. He has eaten better in England. Even prisoners-of-war eat cake in the land of the free.

'Guten Abend, Tante.'

At the sight of him she begins to clatter her saucepans together, 'Abend Kurt. You come alone then?'

It is said in that tone of voice that craftily poses a dozen other questions. He adopts the righteous stance of the responsible husband. 'I've been all the way over to Hemmenstein – buying linen for curtains. I borrowed Manfred Braun's bike. I've just returned it.'

'Not dancing this evening, Junge?'

'Cathy can't dance. She's never learned how to.'

'You could teach her.'

'Ach, ja. There will be plenty of time for that.'

'So she sits by herself in the evenings.'

'She makes curtains.'

'Exciting!'

'She is my wife. Excitement enough I should think for any woman.'

Tante Emma laughs: a rusty, unusual sound. 'You don't change much do you? But you be careful boy! She's English. You will push her so far and no further. No need to scowl like that: she has not complained about you – how could she? You don't even attempt to teach her our language.'

'It's easier if we speak English together.'

'Not for her it isn't. But she understands German without your help: she also reads German too. I've seen her read papers.'

He shifts uneasily in his chair. 'She doesn't fit in,' he blurts, 'it's the way she behaves. I don't like it. All this reading and writing in notebooks: my mother was never like that.'

'Your mother wasn't English,' says Tante dryly; 'and another thing Kurt, your wife looks ill: is she pregnant?'

He looks gloomy. 'Well, she hasn't told me. But if she was I doubt if she'd even notice. She either stares out of the window or talks about poetry and witches.'

'She hardly eats anything Kurt, except for the food she has here when she helps in the kitchen. She gives you her rations. I suppose you know that much.' He is silent. 'She is not happy Kurt. Annaliese saw something the other day. A woman spat on your wife, in the street. Did she tell you?'

'No.'

'Things will get better soon, Junge. They have to. But for now, do not be so unbending, so proud. It can't be easy for you to live with the victor's daughter. But you married her, boy: and you brought her here.'

He has never been able to take advice with good grace: and his aunt's words rankle. The women conspire against him. Even his Tante Emma his father's beloved sister; always his favourite. This Cathy is tougher than she looks: he knows it. She has shown neither fear nor respect for the British colonel. He had been misled by her helpless air and those blistered hands in England. Her china-doll appearance: the delicate skin and wide blue eyes are just so much bull-shit. Good English farmer's expression that! He likes it. It expresses his meaning exactly. He thinks that one way and another, he has been thoroughly swindled: and someone will suffer for it!

He doesn't like people to see him climbing the steps of the Polizei Amt, so he creeps through the yard at the back, avoiding the obstacles of official dustbins and stacks of split logs. He gives her considerate warning of his approach, clattering his shoes on the stairs, in case she is crying.

The door opens up to a rare smell of beeswax polish and flowers. Two hastily-stitched, slightly uneven curtains hang at one window. A jam-jar of roses stands on the pinewood dresser. Potatoes are brown and crisp in the frying-pan. She has brushed her hair and put on her best blue dress.

He can see straight away that the quarrel has shattered her coolness and he is determined that this time, at least, he will take full advantage of it: love does not happen that way with her, very often. He removes the frying-pan from the hot-plate, and turns out the light. Lovemaking between the English, he thinks, must be a very chancy business, dependent on snatched opportunities and favourable omens. But nothing good, his father once told him, ever came easy.

*

He is suddenly jealous of Bruno. Cathy has novelty value, and that can be heady stuff for a boy like his cousin. Bruno was several years younger, had marched with the Hitler Youth on a Sunday. Sunburnt knees, small shorts, waving banners. All that Hitler crap. While Kurt was practising the art of seduction in among the dunes at Swinemünde, Bruno was raising his arm and shouting 'Sieg Heil!' with the rest of the boys.

'You spend too much time with my cousin.'

'He's gentle and quiet: and he speaks to me in German.'

'I have to work overtime in the quarry. I fill four times as many wagons as Bruno. We need money: talk will not buy us bread.'

He thinks she is over-anxious to change the subject. 'The postman's wife will be having her baby soon. I expect they hate me.'

'Why should the postman hate you?'

'He lost his arm in the war: and they live in that dreadful shack down by the railway. We have a better room than they do.'

'Nobody hates you.' This sort of conversation embarrasses him: he will avoid it whenever he can.

'Even you hate me sometimes.'

'That is a lie.'

'Well, you never say that you love me.'

'Love is for doing, not saying. Men who talk too much are no good in bed.'

'I am a disappointment to you,' she says sadly. He cannot deny it. 'Perhaps you should have married a German girl after all. You and I have so little in common.'

The Silesian girl comes into his mind: the dark and tumescent barmaid. Now there was an acquiescent woman if ever he saw one!

*

A sticky heat presses down on the village, and lightning flickers among the hills: rare for September. It rains for a brief ten minutes, an uneven shower that dries at once in the dusty road, but fails to clear the air. Bruno disappears for a day and a night. The postman has got a daughter: the blankets on the pram are pink. Bruno, says Kurt, has probably found himself a girlfriend at last. The week-end begins on a Saturday afternoon. He has washed and shaved and put on the emerald trousers: notching the belt even tighter. He has lost thirty pounds in weight since leaving England.

Kurt is a tidy man. The odds and ends of life are never allowed to spoil the shape of his clothing. He is the one who turns pockets inside out to remove the accumulations of fluff and shredded tobacco that gather in corners. He never has time anymore to wear the emerald jacket. It hangs on his side of the wardrobe, pockets all empty. As far as he knows. Cathy is at her usual station, watching the street from the open window. He sits on the edge of the bed and calls to her softly. She does not even turn round. Several minutes elapse before he concludes he is being punished.

'OK. So what is it this time?'

Her face, when she turns, is the blazing white she has shown to the British colonel.

'Gottes Wille,' he mutters, 'why do you look at me like that?'

She produces a crumpled envelope, like a conjuror, from nowhere. 'Who is this Hildegarde person, and why is she writing you letters?'

'You have dared to search my pockets?'

'I wanted to please you. I was brushing your clothes – the way you ordered me to. You should have been more careful, shouldn't you? If you had been here an hour ago I would have knifed you.'

He laughs: not certain if she is joking. 'You are not strong enough Liebchen, to scratch my little finger.'

'I will kill you if I find out for certain that you have been unfaithful.' There is venom in her face: she is not joking. Jealousy has wrought a miracle in her. She no longer dreams: her whole attention is focused upon him. She is a woman aimed and loaded, and ready to fire.

'You haven't answered my question, lieber husband.'

'There is nothing to tell.'

'Perhaps I should talk to your Tante Emma. She has been trying to warn me of something ever since I came here. Oh, what a fool I've been. I've allowed you to give me orders as if I were one of your Wehrmacht. Yes sir, no sir, please can I polish your shoes sir! Well, you've got your revenge for all the humiliations they put on you in England. Isn't that what it's all about? aren't you punishing me?'

She has not raised her voice. The bitterness drips quietly on his head. She sits straight and unmoving in her chair, the tears making puddles in her hands.

'Nothing good ever comes of reading other people's letters,' he says lamely. 'If you had minded your business none of this would have happened.'

'I would have found you out, sooner or later. Now I know where you go in the evenings: and why you will never take me out dancing. You hate being embarrassed don't you, and what would you do if your barmaid and I came face to face?'

'It is not what you think.' He sounds desperate. 'I only talk to this woman; she speaks my dialect; she has taken nothing from you; she is a widow and lonely. That is all.'

'This is a pretty passionate letter from a woman you only talk to. You accused me of cheating and lying. Well, now we are even. There are things you don't know about me, husband. I am a bitch. I never forgive a hurt, and you have betrayed me.'

'Mein Gott,' he cries, 'you speak as if you are the Christ and I am the Judas. So what has happened here? I talk to a woman, she fancies me, writes me a silly letter. Do you think I am a love-sick boy playing games?'

'I think you are in a chancy position Kurt. Make up your mind: an English wife or German. Life in the East or the West. There is still time to undo the knot we tied in Kingsbridge.'

'Is that what you want?'

'I don't know, you are not the man I took you to be. We have different values.'

He makes an angry gesture. 'And what do you know about my values: little English pigeon that has never before left the nest? War changes a man, makes him hard. I have been eight years away from my family. I have lived among men in barracks and prison camps: have forgotten the gentle ways of women. I am a hard master to you, that is true. But there is no place for softness anymore in my country. Look at those women out there; they work all day in the fields with their men. They are Kameraden not weeping schoolgirls.'

'That's important to you isn't it? that word Kameraden: it has a special meaning, untranslatable into English.' She swings back to face him again. 'They are watching us you know. Your countrymen and mine: our families. Waiting for the big explosion. That marriage won't work, they say, how can it? English and German: the old protagonists. How can love grow between them? You are full of hatred Kurt, but you don't seem to know it: and that hatred spills over and touches me, even when you don't mean it.'

She tosses the crumpled letter in his direction. 'I don't think much of your taste in women. The Gasthof barmaid – and you are teetotal. Explain that away – if you can.'

She has, as usual, laid down the routes, but failed to provide him with the map. Her arguments are too subtle, and so he retreats into silence.

Couples who live in one room should never quarrel. The words should be stitched in a sampler and hung on the wall. There is no space for her tears or his uneasy conscience. He thinks that the walls might as well buckle inwards upon them. He has never apologised to a woman. He is the man: his façade must remain intact. It is all he has left.

Hildegarde's room smells of kümmel and drying washing. She invites him in to a sulky silence, letting him know that he is long overdue. 'Cat got your tongue?' she asks, in that multi-purpose voice that his aunt has taken to using lately.

Ach ja! spitting, clawing English cat has got his tongue. But he can't tell Hildegarde that.

'How goes it then Kurt? I heard how they had to give you a special room when your wife fetched the big guns out from Hanover.'

'It wasn't Cathy's doing. Well – not exactly.'

'How was it then mein lieber? Exactly.' Her sarcasm flays him. He thinks he doesn't know anything any more. Is trapped neatly between blunt German directness, and polite English prevarication. God damn the victors who have split his tongue, his loyalty, his country.

'I should not have come here Hilde. It was a mistake.'

She lays a hand on his sleeve: moves closer, and speaks to him in the dialect of Pommern. 'We are not children Kurt. I won't wait forever.' This Hildegarde, he thinks, knows well the full value of nostalgia.

*

The letter comes to him from Bad Salzuflen, via the Home Office, London, England. 'In view of the fact that your wife is English we have decided to re-admit you into the United Kingdom.'

*

The pain of the autumn days is upon him. A low-slung sun slants its shadow across the limestone, and daily the beech forests alter colour. In the valleys the farmers are lifting the sugar-beet and potatoes, and beginning the winter ploughing. The yearning for land is a physical ache in his guts. There are nights when he lies alone at the forest's edge, and weeps for the plains and the village far out of his reach, beyond the Oder.

The crisis comes, as he knows it has to, on the day when Cathy says, 'Well, that's it Kurt, I've had enough of all this. I am going home.'

He asks her why, out of habit.

'Because I find it impossible to live with you – in your country.'

Cathy. December 1948

She feels safe in the train. Already latched tight into the long cold journey, and cut off from all responsibility. Even the brooding figure of Kurt in the opposite corner cannot frighten her now. She didn't believe he was actually coming with her until she saw him heave the suitcases into the luggage van. Perhaps now, while the train waits in Hanover station, there will be time for him to change his mind and walk away. But impulsive behaviour of that sort is not in his nature: he will never make any move without first considering all the implications. He sits up straight in his corner seat; he looks belligerent and braced to take on the world. Every blond hair lies in its appointed place, and his trouser creases are razor sharp. Cathy knows that she should be feeling pity for him at such a moment, but she has drawn so far back inside herself that she scarcely recognises the needs of others. This time they haven't talked it over. There have been none of those intimate whispered conversations about the wisdom of living in his country or hers. She had delivered her ultimatum: she will not allow him an armistice, or even an honourable defeat. He must capitulate unconditionally, or remain in Germany.

Her ability to impose her will upon him takes her by surprise. 'Don't come to England unless you really want to,' she says: afraid that too easy a victory might somehow rebound upon her. But he packs his suitcases without a sign of reproach. He includes the old photographs his mother has rescued from the Russian occupation of their home; and they lie, like lavender sachets, among his threadbare clothing, and the few possessions he has accumulated since returning to his Fatherland. Her withdrawal from him is deliberate and self-defensive: the way a hand is pulled back from a red-hot surface. The little pulse of love that remains is so tentative and fragile, that he may destroy it, and her, with one pressure of his finger, and send her wandering and defenceless back to England.

The train doors slam and the whistle blows. People are leaning out of carriage windows and calling their last farewells to relatives on the platform. Hanover station, partially resurrected since her arrival there, six months ago, begins to slide past the window, and she is glad to see it go. Her goodbyes have been said in Dietkirchendorf: regretfully to Tante Emma who has been her only friend. The romantic Weserbergland has not lived up to its promise. She hopes she will never set foot in it again.

The train gathers speed; it is aimed and pointing at home: so why does she continue to feel uneasy? She shivers inside her lightweight summer coat, and longs for the good Harris tweed she has left behind in Kingsbridge. Kurt wears his emerald suit and his old brown prisoner's overcoat. It is the only adequate clothing he possesses. They are, she reflects, truly poor; and it is no longer the patched-over, thinned-down poverty, that had seemed honourable in wartime. Their combined possessions fill four suitcases: and they, are, of course, homeless again. Anxiety hovers over her like a cloud. Kurt is so silent and unapproachable in his corner. She looks for a single word: so that she might have the satisfaction of telling herself – this is what he is! But there is no single word. Sometimes he goes away in directions where she may not follow: and then she grows nervous, and uses desperate tactics to haul him back.

She leans forward now, and touches his knee. 'I want you to understand.'

'Understand what?'

'Why I couldn't live in your country.'

He presses his lips together: he will not make it easy for her.

'I grew up among easy-going people. We managed to live quite happily without cleaning our shoes and pressing our clothes every time we wore them.'

He gives no hint of comprehension, and she can feel her temper rising. Her reasons for going home are not the ones she speaks out loud; she thinks he knows it. Knows how she fears all the other girls who look at him with covetous eyes: the taller, thicker girls of positive substance, the ones who speak his native tongue, who move to his body's rhythms.

'You'll have to learn to live with all my inadequacies: but you won't mind that so much in my country will you? It won't be so obvious there.' That shaft flies home. She sees his eyelids flicker. Her anger dissolves into tears. 'Were you ashamed of me: the china doll, the speechless puppet. Did you apologise for me when my back was turned?

He sighs. 'Why do you start these arguments Cathy? You ask a question, and then you make your own answer; you don't like the answer you have made – and so you cry. You are not logical.'

'What has logic to do with it. You don't love me do you?'

'I am coming with you: what more do you want from me?'

She sees the way he glances uneasily at the other two occupants of the compartment. Embarrassed again: she knows he is praying that neither of them can understand English.

'Well you didn't have to come with me. Always remember that. I didn't make you.'

He leans out towards her and places his hand on her knee. 'You couldn't live without me,' he tells her complacently, 'admit it and be an obedient wife, and then we shall both be happy.'

In this case he knows her better than she knows herself. Not a comfortable thought to live with. Knows that with her he had been the first; her introduction to life as it is lived by flesh and blood people. He had not come to her from between the printed pages of some leather bound volume, but on his own two strong legs. He is a man: good and bad in measurable proportions, not to be laid away on a bookshelf at her whim. Would she have left him if her poor resolution had been put to the test? She knows that she cannot, never will, hold her grudge against him: and knows too that once committed, she will never be able to turn back.

*

The ashtray is brimming over with cigarette ends, which means that the nervous girl has been on the train since it left Berlin. She offers her cigarettes around and saves her smile for Kurt, who accepts both gifts with alacrity, and says that his wife does not care to smoke. The man in the opposite seat must be very old. He has a continuous tremor in his limbs, which makes it difficult for him to hold the briefcase on his knees. His head is closely shaved, and bears several livid scars across the crown, where small tufts of snow white hair are beginning to grow back in. He dribbles a little from one side of his mouth, and mops at it furtively with his handkerchief. Cathy feels revulsion at the sight of him: and then shame at the thinness of her pity.

The man uses the German language like a rusty tool whose purpose he has forgotten. He wishes them Guten-tag, and then begins to hunt for words.

'How long – how far – where are you all going?'

In unison they answer, 'England.'

'Such lucky people' he says, glaring at Cathy. 'What does a man have to do these days to deserve such fortune. Would they allow a man like me to visit your country?'

Kurt answers swiftly, 'My wife speaks no German.'

'So – you married an Engländerin. That was a clever move: if you can't beat them – join them.'

In a heavy Berlin accent the girl interrupts him. 'Oh why don't you shut up Grandad. What the hell has it got to do with you, who marries whom, and why?'

'I've just come back from Russia,' he says, as if she had never spoken. 'I've been in a prison camp for the past five years.' He looks over to Cathy. 'Did they tell you about the Russians, lady? Did they tell you the sort of things they do to women?'

'Why don't you tell me?' the German girl asks. 'Why don't you try out all your nasty stories on one of your own nationality?' She leans heavily into the ashtray, and squeezes the cigarette end as if it were the throat of some captive Ivan or Boris.

'Come on then Grandpa: let us swap yarns, you and me: see who can make the English girl vomit first. She understands German well enough: look at her face! You men are a pain in the arse. Five years in a prison camp and you think you've suffered. You couldn't have had it worse than we did in Berlin in '45. Where were you then, you valiant German soldiers, when the women in Dahlem and Wilmersdorf were jumping from six-storey windows? We had our share, mein lieber, and don't you forget it. I was a kid of thirteen years – how old were you?'

The man's tremor intensifies as he struggles to open his briefcase. His words come out thick and ugly with his uncontrolled saliva. 'I'll show you how old I am, you bitch! Here, take a look at my papers. I was born in 1920. I am twenty-eight years old.' Tears begin to course down his face; he pulls out a tattered photo and thrusts it across to the girl. 'Look at this if you don't believe me. This is how I looked in 1943.'

The picture is passed to Kurt, who studies it briefly, and hands it over to Cathy. It shows a slender, dark haired boy in the uniform of the Luftwaffe. She compares it with the ruined face of the man beside her, and feels her own tears rising.

'What in God's name did they do to you?' The German girl asks, in a different voice.

'I don't know. I can't remember.' He turns to Kurt, 'Will you remind me to get off the train when we reach Bielefeld. Sometimes I forget what I have to do. They said that my brother will meet me at the station,' there is panic in his voice, 'but how will he recognise me? What shall I do? Must I march up and down the platform shouting "My name is Willi Meyer" – who will claim me?'

They consider the man's predicament; but it is only the girl who attempts to reassure him. 'Don't worry,' she tells him gently, 'they'll be so glad to have you back: the way that you look won't matter. My brother lost both his legs at Stalingrad. But he came back: that was the miracle. The only thing that counted.'

Cathy makes no attempt to join in the conversation. She is always doubly nervous of using her shaky German in Kurt's presence, and the sight of the weeping man is becoming more than she can bear. There is a limit to the absorbency of the human mind, and lately hers has been saturated by other people's pain.

She looks at Kurt; his thinness, and the score of cuts on his hands from the handling of limestone can be considered as being no more than a mark of health, by the man from Russia. Her husband's head with its thatch of thick blond hair is drooping apologetically upon his chest: and she begins to feel a fierce and awful pleasure at the sight of Kurt's unexpected humiliation. She is glad that he will have to endure the shame of his health, and physical perfection all the way to Bielefeld and the Dutch frontier.

She is shocked by the unaccustomed honesty of her thoughts. This brutal frankness of Germans with one another is becoming contagious. They rarely indulge in polite evasion, or prevaricate over important matters. Perhaps she should use the same blunt tactics with Kurt. Tell him about the hundred ways he crucifies her tenderest feelings for him. Her jealousy and the fear that he might desert her. But that would be to put weapons in his hand: and he has more than enough of those already.

The man at her side falls asleep quite suddenly: a child exhausted from crying. He shudders at intervals as if he dreams. As they near Bielefeld Kurt leans across and shakes him gently by the sleeve. The man wakes at once, cringing as if he expects a blow.

Kurt says, 'You asked me to remind you to get off the train at Bielefeld; we're pulling in now. Are these your cases?'

The man moves stiffly, lacking co-ordination. Kurt helps him down to the platform, and settles his luggage tidily beside him.

Cathy sees how anxiously the man peers at the faces beyond the ticket barrier. Nobody cries out 'Here is my brother. Here is Willi Meyer!' Nobody claims him.

*

As soon as the formalities at the Dutch frontier are completed, Cathy sees how quickly her husband and the dark haired girl discover each other's presence in the compartment. Soon, they are deep in conversation, and her exclusion is complete.

The girl has a wan and feverish prettiness which she inspects regularly in her handbag mirror. She renews her lipstick, and fiddles with her hair. She checks the seams of her stockings to draw attention to her legs. Cathy, who can sit motionless for hours and scarcely bat an eyelash finds this activity wearing, and quite unnecessary.

Kurt is clearly reconciled again to the vigour of his healthy body. He smiles and is over-courteous from the throne of his corner seat. Cathy resents the easy charm of his manner towards other women. She knows herself to be gauche and shy with other men.

Inge Zeigenfelz possesses a certain city chic: the kind of sophistication that was lacking in the Fräuleins of Dietkirchendorf. She is precisely the sort of girl Cathy fears most. The smart black handbag is crammed to the top with chocolates and cigarettes which can only have come from a British Naafi, or American PX. The Berlin accent is a difficult one to follow, but Cathy's need to interpret the conversation becomes imperative.

'I'm on my way to Yorkshire in England,' Inge says to Kurt. My fiancé is a sergeant in the British Airforce. We are to be married in a town called Huddersfield.' She waves a pale left hand which bears an engagement ring, and pauses as if she expects a round of applause for effort. She leans towards Kurt with a winning smile, 'Can you tell me if Huddersfield is anywhere near London?'

He turns to Cathy for guidance but she has completely

absented herself this time. She coldly disclaims all knowledge of Huddersfield and Yorkshire. She gives her attention to Holland, and is rewarded sooner than she expects.

The December dusk is creeping across the fields, and in the dark window glass she can see her husband's reflection. As he bends to light the German girl's cigarette, he makes sure that their fingers touch and linger. Cathy is tempted to open the carriage door and push Inge Zeigenfelz out of the moving train. The trend of her jealous thoughts appals her. Is this how murder is committed? Such a gentle, passive girl for all these twenty years, and this German husband has turned her into a vigilante: a scrutineer; a sentry, on guard to protect her closest interests.

She looks back at Kurt and sees that innocence shines on his face: but his eyes are bright with challenge. This is obviously going to be his test case. He will inform her that he has no intention of forgoing all contact with other women, because she thinks she has caught him out once before with Hildegarde Seifert. Perhaps it is only normal young man's vanity, this need he has to prove his desirability to every woman he meets: the thought makes her feel mature, until she remembers that she is hardly competent to judge him. He has been her first, her last, her only man.

*

Holland is flat and endless: there is nothing outside the window to distract her attention from her husband. He is showing off a little, now, describing for Inge the life as lived by the Anglo-Saxons. The primitive island people.

'You will find English houses cold in the winter. They have these open coal fires, and no double windows: and the plumbing is fixed to the outer walls so that when it freezes the pipes all burst, and the house is flooded.' He taps his forehead with a significant finger. 'But they are cheerful people. They don't seem to mind about setbacks.' He glances at Cathy, 'At least, most of them don't.'

So he is an authority on the English now, she thinks bitterly, after three years confinement in one of our prison camps. She closes her eyes and tries to imagine Kingsbridge. She wants to call up her parents' house but finds that Dietkirchendorf has intervened and will not let her go. She is no longer the girl who has travelled this route six months ago. She has been subjected to pressure and found wanting. Insight tells her this failure is bound to cost her dearly.

Inge, meanwhile, is smoking hard and reminiscing. She has reached the point in her story where the victorious British Army is advancing into Berlin. 'They were very polite. Polite and distant: as if they couldn't risk dirtying their clean hands on us. But they were quiet, well-disciplined men, and we were grateful for that much.' She draws her breath in sharply through pinched nostrils, 'But the "muzhiks" had got to us first, mein Lieber. Ach Gott, but you should have seen them. Mongolian animals, with slit-eyes and flat brown faces. Like drunken apes they were, with the stink of schnapps upon them, and the vodka running out of their ears. The dead were piled up to the window sills on our street. Nowhere to run: fire behind us and Russians in front. Our flat was six floors up, but those bastards found us. My mother and sisters were lucky: they died; they threw themselves out of the window. I was not so fortunate. They caught me with one leg across the window-sill. Ah well!' She sighed and drew deeply on her cigarette, 'I got myself a prize in the end. I bagged me an Engländer.'

Kurt's face shows shock and something else: he glances uneasily at Cathy. 'Is that all you feel for him? this sergeant?'

Inge grins: a knowing, urban grin that marks her down as a survivor. 'It's not hard to guess where you come from, country boy. You had it bloody easy, sitting out the end of the war in a cosy billet like England.' She no longer bothers to hide her contempt. 'I would love any man,' she says, 'who could give me security and sixty Players a day.'

At the sight of Kurt's flushed face, she begins to laugh. 'You know, mein Lieber, the Russians even re-named all the streets and squares in their part of Berlin. You woke up one morning and found you were living on Volga Strasse. They nailed up life-sized pictures of Stalin where Hitler's used to hang. My God it was funny. Mensch! We almost died of laughing.'

'Wilmersdorf,' says Kurt, snatching at a name, 'do you know it?'

'I should,' says Inge, 'I was born on Himburger Strasse.'

'What about the old Stettiner Bahnof,' he asks, 'is it still standing, do the trains still run East from there?'

'The Russians made us rip out the railway lines,' she says dryly, 'and nobody's travelling East any more. Haven't you heard country boy? It's gone out of fashion.'

City bitch, thinks Cathy: and she feels a rare protectiveness towards her German husband. He is out of his depth this time: and he doesn't even know it.

*

They travel in silence for hours. A constraint grows up between husband and wife, so that they move automatically from train to ship, and back to train again, without a word being spoken.

Inge Zeigenfelz vanishes among the dockside crowds at Harwich, but her going makes little difference. Kurt is displeased and he makes his feelings known.

'You behaved like a child.'

'When?' she asks, although she already knows.

'On the train. You turned your back and refused to talk to that girl.'

'From where I was sitting, you were being friendly enough for both of us.'

'You see! You are jealous again. What is it with you – that girl was frightened. Coming into a foreign country she needed some reassurance.'

'She'll be all right. She's the type who always falls on her feet. She'll at least find food in the English shops, and milk on her doorstep.' Cathy pauses, and says with deliberate venom, 'And she will also have the advantage of having an English husband.'

A muscle is twitching in his jaw. 'So that is it,' he says quietly, 'I had not thought you could be cruel. I was mistaken.'

All at once she feels frightened: the minute the words are out she wants to recall them. Instead she will seek for justification.

'Well, you shouldn't treat me as if I'm a raw recruit, or a puppy that's broken its training. I am a woman, and it's time you realise it.'

'A woman?' He shakes his head: 'You are a stupid child. I should never have taken you from your parents.'

Part Four

1979

Catherine Baumann returned to her corner seat in the compartment, and picked up her volume of Thomas Mann, but did not open it. Instead, she nodded towards the window. 'Perhaps I should have stayed here in 1948: I panicked you know, and ran home to England.'

'Your stay in my country was rather a short one,' Jürgen Hecht's tone was sardonic. 'But,' he relented, 'I can't really blame you. At least you found enough courage to make a stand, and take the risk that he might not go with you.' He hesitated. 'My first marriage was absolute hell. In the end I had a breakdown: I attempted suicide, and spent a year in a mental hospital. As a result of all that, I divorced her, but in the process, of course, I lost my son and daughter. That much I do regret.'

'How old were your children at that time?'

'One was ten, the other six. I was a rotten father,' he confessed, 'the whole atmosphere was poisoned between us. They were better off without me. I like to think now that I could perhaps have been a well-loved Papa, and grandfather: surrounded by doting offspring. But there was no precedent for that kind of thing in my family. Well, unhappy children usually grow up to breed the next generation of lousy parents don't they?'

'Was your childhood so unhappy?'

'My mother taught violin and piano; my lessons began at the age of three. I wanted to be a concert pianist, but my father was an important and active member of the Nazi Party. He had very different plans for my future. Between them, they managed to tear me apart. I never made the concert platform, and I must have been the most cowardly airman in all the Third Reich. Yes,' he went on, thoughtfully, 'the relationships that break up a marriage often go back further than we can appreciate at the time. We marry in youth, determined to make our bid for freedom. When all the time we are dragging our parents into the marriage bed with us. All the old sins are compounded: mistakes repeated: wrong attitudes carried forward.' He sighed; 'Such damage we do in the name of love.'

Kingsbridge 1949

Cathy's state of mind has always hinged from day to day on the approbation of others. She has always been sensitive to the approval of those people who are closest to her: and marriage has only intensified this dependence. To return to Kingsbridge has not been easy, and now, she is neatly caught in a trap of her own devising: acutely aware of her parents' disapproval, and of the ambiguous state of affairs that exists between Kurt and herself. The house in Laburnum Avenue has contracted during her absence: and she finds the comparative luxury of her parents' home constrictive, after the spartan poverty of the room on Hauptstrasse. Ground that has always been stable is shifting: and the parents whose word she has feared and respected have lost much of their power to alarm her. Dependence has been transferred: and security will in future depend on her husband's approbation. A powerful weapon in the hands of a man she loves, but does not altogether trust.

She would like to forget certain happenings, but the memory of that day when she held Hildegarde Seifert's letter in her hand has ploughed a deep furrow. How could he when only six months before they had stood side by side, and promised a solemn, not-to-be-broken vow that there would never be anyone else for either of them? He had put a wedding ring on her finger, and according to the custom of his country she had slipped a matching ring onto his. It had all been for nothing. She recognises a growing tendency to indulge in self-pity: but who else will weep for her? Her marriage is to be one of those miracles in which the whole will in some mysterious way turn out to be so much more than the sum of the component parts. She even imagines that she can heal the hurts he has suffered: and in so doing, discover her own salvation.

She tries to take a step backwards, grab a little perspective: but as long as they live in her parents' house she knows an evaluation will be pointless. Old loyalties fight with new ones, tugging her this way and that.

Kurt's exuberance disturbs her parents' middle-aged view of what is right and proper. His wide shoulders loom large in every room, and she too, often finds his robustness embarrassing to cope with. He has always, in spite of his frequent anger, been a loving and demonstrative man. She has rarely been able to pass him by without having him lay a caressing hand upon her. It has seemed quite a natural gesture in his country: back in Kingsbridge she finds all her old inhibitions returning. 'Don't be quite so loving in front of my parents,' she whispers, 'it's not done in England – at least not in public.'

He grins. 'I heard about that,' he says, 'it is said that the Englishman only makes love in the dark.'

It is not exactly a merry Christmas. They find privacy only in her bedroom, and she worries in case the number of hours they spend there appears indecent.

'You do not love me the same since we came to England.' It is his turn now to complain of feeling neglected: 'We must find our own place.' She agrees; but the knowledge that he needs her is all that she really wants: and why not indeed? In Kingsbridge, England, he has no one else.

*

'Kurt asked me the other day about his chances of leasing land. A smallholding he said; or something similar.' Her father touches a flaming match to a pipe of tobacco that is already drawing well: a sure sign that he is about to deliver an ultimatum. 'Well, I've made some enquiries and it seems that he won't be allowed to set up in business on his own.'

'Why ever not?' she demands, 'he's done nothing wrong.'

'He is classed as an ex-enemy alien,' her father points out, 'and in any case you don't have a penny between you.'

'There may be another chance,' her father continues, 'I know a man who is looking for someone to manage a farm. He's a naval captain who spends most of his time at sea. He inherited the place when his father died, and the latest bailiff has brought him right to the verge of bankruptcy. I've been out there,' her father admits, 'to look the place over. It has a phone, and mains electricity – and a first-class farmhouse.' The implication in the final word is clear.

'But will he employ a German?' she asks.

'He'll employ any responsible man – he said so.'

Reluctantly she tells Kurt about the nearly bankrupt farm, and the Captain Penrose who needs a bailiff. 'It sounds like a lonely place. No shops, no library. Only grass and hedges.'

'That will be quite in order for me,' he says decisively, 'you must know that I only like the quiet places in your country: the copses where the little foxes say guten Abend.' He is, she knows, remembering Hobart's farm, and equating it with a lost contentment.

Life, for some people, seems to fall into a pattern. Once again, and this time against her better judgement, Cathy is brought to a valley. The lane leading down to the farm is so steep that they walk stiff-legged to resist its pull. Kurt points out how the rain is caught in the cool green hollow: and how the warmth of the sun will be trapped by surrounding hills. Natural advantages like these, he tells her gravely, are not to be valued lightly. From the tone of his voice, she knows that his mind is made up. Kurt Baumann is unchanging once his course is set, and Cathy would have been wiser in her dealings with him if she had recognised his essential nature earlier and settled for compromise. He is a countryman: not only by birth and inclination, but all the way back, through generations of yeoman farmers.

The name on the gate says *Moorseek Farm.* Two hundred acres of neglected farmland, lying ten miles south of Kingsbridge: with a bus stop a good two miles away, and only a telephone to link her to the civilised world.

'I like your husband,' the owner tells her, 'he knows what he wants in life and I approve of that. Move in as soon as you want to. The job is yours.'

'What did Captain Penrose mean when he said that you know what you want?' she asks, later on.

Kurt laughs: 'I told him that I must have some of the pig and poultry sheds for my own use. If we cannot agree on that – then I am not his man.'

She is appalled: 'Kurt, how could you be so cheeky? you are hardly in a position to dictate your terms to a prospective employer.'

'But natürlich!' He declares. 'I will make that farm productive again and he knows it. He has met Germans before: he knows I will do what I promise. But there must be something in it for me, and I told him so.'

The farmhouse is square and ugly: no thatch or creeper softens its angular outline: no picturesque charm will ever endear it to her. It is just like a small child's drawing: four small casement windows, door set plumb centre, and a stack of sloping chimneys that lean westwards. The rooms are small, and the black-beamed ceilings and tiny windows tend to shut out the daylight: but this is a feature of the house that secretly pleases her. For as long as she can remember, Cathy has shunned the sunlight; her type of skin will not tan she says, but freckle. Like so many of Cathy's statements this is not wholly true.

The trouble had started early in her life. Her eyes would begin to itch and water: a dull pain throbbed on one side of her head, and eventually she would vomit. Excitement at Christmas and birthdays, and the hot bright days of summer, had always aggravated the problem. As she grew older the headaches increased in their frequency and ability to disrupt her life. She rarely ventured too far from home: other children were robust and noisy. Cathy read books, and listened to music; she wrote small poems and gazed out of windows; and because she did so in isolation, the inhibiting circle closed in upon her.

A bad attack would be heralded in by a series of odd sensations. Her hands grew numb, and towering edifices of burning gold zig-zagged across her vision. She kept all knowledge of these phenomena carefully hidden, fearing that she would be laughed at, or scolded for telling lies. This affliction has a name. In medical circles it is known as migraine. By the time she reached adolescence, Cathy had a formula worked out, which explained the whole frightening business to her satisfaction. She had been singled out by God to suffer an episodic madness. The nuns who taught her had a propensity for quoting the apter Bible stories: and hadn't St Paul, himself a sinner, been struck down by a blinding light on the road to Damascus. The headaches were simply a warning from Above that she should control her temper: and it was a fact that, when she remembered to move slowly, speak softly, and avoid argument and dissension, the headaches became less frequent.

Her parents saw only a moody, secretive child who suffered 'bilious bouts' for no definite reason. Cathy's father was an intelligent, artistic man of fluctuating moods and uncertain temper. Her mother's preoccupation in life was to take avoiding action from these highs and lows of her marriage partner. Both parents took for granted that a timorous child would grow into a submissive adult. Until she met Kurt Baumann their daughter had never had more to offer than passive resistance to any directive issued by them. But Cathy knows now, that her parents are watching and biding their time. 'I told you so' is on their lips, although they say nothing. Such painful knowledge is often implicit in families, and never more so than among the Wyatts.

The move away from her parents has been instinctive: up to the age of nineteen she has been such a good girl. But now she suspects that she might have escaped from one form of loving bondage only to find herself submitting to yet another: and this time it is more than mere bondage, it is willing enslavement.

*

Her parents have kindly donated the furniture from her old bedroom: including the pink armchair and the scratched oak bookcase. She finds two worn, but enormous armchairs in a second-hand shop, and the proprietor throws in an old mahogany sideboard, pitted with woodworm as a sign of goodwill.

There is an unexpected pleasure this time in hanging curtains, and making a proper bed with new sheets and blankets. When Cathy performs a domestic task these days, she tries hard to achieve the perfection approved by Kurt. Her former rebellion is cooling now to a cautious reappraisal. If they are to spend a lifetime together, one or other will have to change. Instinct warns her that person will not be Kurt Baumann.

Spring comes early to England in 1949. In late February there are days that are as soft and mild as May. A haze of green lies upon the hawthorn, and in the crowns of the elms. The whole valley is filled with a tentative, trembling magic.

From the upper windows she has a depressing view of overgrown hedges and ditches, the blocked drains, and the arable land where the first crop of weeds is already showing. Kurt only sees advantages. 'The lay-out is perfect,' he tells her. 'Remember the mud and filth on Hobart's? Here, is a concrete yard, with barn and sheds built around it. We have electricity and piped water – no more milking with hand, by lamplight.'

Her guilt is eased: he no longer hungers for Pommern. He is happy, she tells herself: in England he will achieve his heart's desire. It is a remarkable thought, and she does not altogether believe it.

His working day never ends until darkness falls. Even then, he will leave his chair and return to the sheds to check on the newly-purchased stock. 'Captain Penrose told you to advertise for help,' she complains, 'I hardly ever see you. You must be mad to struggle like this when there is no need to.'

His face has a tight and wary expression. 'If I advertise in the newspaper,' he says, 'I cannot be sure who will answer. It will not be good if I have to give orders to Englishmen so soon after war between us.'

'Can't you forget about that,' she cries. 'Put war out of your mind, you are living in England now. Sooner or later you will have to accept our ways, our people.'

He stares in disbelief. 'When did you ever accept my ways, my people? You were more English in Dietkirchendorf than ever you were at Hobart's.' He squeezes his thumb and forefinger tightly together and thrusts them beneath her nose: 'Not that much did you give me of understanding. You moved not one centimeter towards me. Would you make an Engländer of me?' He stands up abruptly, knocking his chair to the floor, 'Never, I tell you. Let the world go under, I will always be German. That is the pride I was born with, and you shall not undermine it.' He picks up his chair, and sets it firmly back on its feet.

'So you are loyal to your country,' she shouts back, 'so what does that amount to? A silly sense of indebtedness to a few square yards of dirt? Born in a different time, in another place, you would have been someone else.'

'Clever book-talk,' he snaps, 'like everything else you say it has no real meaning.'

She begins to rub her right eye, and the first of the headache pains slices through her temple. The truce has not lasted long. But she had never expected that it would.

*

News travels fast in the country. It becomes known, via the man who collects the milk-churns, that the new German bailiff at Moorseek is in urgent need of a cowman. A small wooden bungalow goes with the job, it is said, as well as free milk and electricity.

Cathy hears the motorbike engine long before it has breasted the hill, and she is half-expecting to see the man who wears helmet and goggles. He roars into the yard at a speed which scatters the hens and causes the ancient horse to bolt. Kitted out from head to foot in shiny black leather, and swaggering boldly, he looks an unlikely prospect.

'Please wait,' she tells him, 'I'll fetch my husband.' But the man strides ahead of her, into the dairy; stripping off helmet and goggles as he goes.

'I hear-a you look for a cowman,' he says to Kurt.

'That is correct. Can you milk with machine?'

He makes an expansive gesture, 'I do-a every job on farm. I verry good herdsman.' Rather superfluously he adds, 'I Italiano – what country you? Is-a true you're a German?'

Kurt answers stiffly, 'I am German.'

The Italian tips his head to one side and winks in conspiratorial fashion. 'I no like-a the English.' He taps his forehead significantly and nods: 'I think same like-a you. I understand very good with Germans.'

Kurt looks embarrassed. 'My wife is English,' he warns.

The Italian turns at once to where Cathy is standing in shadow. 'Scusi signora,' he grins, bowing low from the waist. 'I love all the English ladies.' He kisses his fingertips to her, 'Ah,' he sighs deeply, 'ah, the beautiful English ladies.'

'Why did you leave your last job?' Kurt asks with sudden suspicion.

The Italian shrugs: sounds defensive. 'Is-a not my fault if that farmer's wife, she love me a leetle. He is jealous man – he chase me away with big dogs.'

Kurt laughs: 'Is that all?' Cathy thinks he sounds relieved; he himself, of course, need never have any fears on that score.

*

Sante Simeoni is one of those prisoners-of-war who has elected to stay on in England. He moves into the wooden bungalow which stands in the shade of the oak tree, behind the barn. Cathy gives him a pair of unbleached linen curtains (once bartered for soap and coffee), and he buys a bed and a table, and a sagging blue armchair. The rest of his needs are supplied by the various girls who appear in the lane each evening. One brings a rug for the floor; another, a small stove for cooking. This Italian it seems, has all the right contacts.

Cathy finds him faintly alarming. The contrast between her stolid husband and this volatile man is pronounced; she cannot imagine them working together. The Italian has black curling hair and a fresh, high colour. He is thin, with that bitter profile found on old Roman coins. He only resembles Kurt in his neatness; there is an economic deftness in Sante's movements: a hint of strength, coiled, and to spare.

April comes in gently with alternate hours of rain and sunshine. The grass grows emerald and high right across the valley, and down to the river fields, exactly as Kurt had predicted. But the years of neglect bring another growth in the fields. Pale acres of winter wheat now struggle for space between rampant beds of wild marigold and chickweed. Ditches and brooks overflow;

fence posts have rotted and need renewing; gates swing on broken hinges, and cowsheds and calf pens are filthy. The barn is cluttered with heaps of rotting sacking and broken machinery, which harbour rats.

The two men begin to work like a team in harness. 'The most urgent jobs must be done before haymaking starts,' they agree. They tackle the gates and fences: new fence posts are cut and driven in, and the wire between them renewed and strung taut. The farm gates are made to swing level on oiled hinges, and are fastened with proper latches, instead of old bits of fraying string. The barn is swept clean and the rats destroyed; the cowsheds and and calf pens whitewashed.

In between all this, the Friesian herd must be milked and fed, night and morning.

Cathy, quite alone in the house, feels unusually healthy. She scrubs and polishes, hangs pictures, blackleads the old iron cooking range until it shines, and sews cushions. She has not suffered a headache for several weeks now.

One evening, she idly watches the rooks in the elm-trees, and it occurs to her that she too has the nesting urge. The idea is novel: she has never, in her life, even touched a baby, or held one in her arms. She pursues the thought to its only conclusion. She is already pregnant. On the following day she visits Kingsbridge. After supper that evening she says abruptly, 'I'm pregnant.'

Kurt nods behind his copy of *Farmers' Weekly*. 'I thought you might be,' he says.

'Well you could have said so.'

He shrugs, 'It is women's business to know such things. Better that you should find out for yourself.'

'But how will I manage, stuck here, on a farm, miles from the hospital and with only a horse for transport?'

'I take good care of you,' he assures her, 'don't worry. I have never lose calf or foal or piglet.'

'But I'm not an animal,' she wails, 'I'm a woman.'

'Birth is same for us all,' he tells her, 'and Sante is very skilled herdsman. Between us we manage.'

*

The summer of 1949 is a good one; the sun shines for eight or nine hours every day. In spite of the heat and the sunlight. Cathy's rare sense of well-being persists. She is no longer lonely: she needs the space her isolation gives her, to clear out old lumber from her mind and make room for new thoughts.

The weather holds and the hay is cut. Kurt drives the swathe turner up and down the shorn fields in the evenings, turning the grass in a long slow arc in the drying wind. The first calf is born from a little black heifer called Victory. When he comes from the shed with his hands all bloodied, she asks, 'Is the calf alive: is the mother all right?'

He grins. 'Do not worry so much: when your time is come I will do as well for you. I am damned fine midwife.'

Before he sleeps, Kurt talks of his plans for the future. As soon as he has enough money saved he will buy hens and a sow. He will sell eggs, and weaner pigs in the market: and when the time is right, he will lease his own land. He never speaks of the coming child.

The bottom drawer of the sideboard is slowly filling up with small white garments. She is proud of her new knitting skills: having only recently mastered the trick of keeping the stitches on the needles. Her mother gives her an old wicker crib, and she lines it with soft white muslin. The pram is delivered from a shop in the town: and again, she searches Kurt's face for some sign of approval.

But it is Sante Simeoni who comes in to view the smart grey coachwork and gleaming chrome. 'My mama has put me in leetle wooden box,' he confides, 'she pulla-me everywhere with piece of string. Italiano baby not have-a pram – not cry much!'

'How many are there in your family?'

'Fourteen boys, one sister. Three of my brothers are priest. I am – how you say – black sheep of my family.'

'Why do you stay in England?' asks Cathy. 'Don't you miss them?'

He shrugs: 'If I go home my papa he find me a wife. Her papa will find us a house. Soon we have many children. In England – I do as I like.'

It is true. At least a dozen girls come to live with Sante that summer. He allows them to stay for a week or two: contribute a saucepan or bright woollen cushion towards his comfort, and then he will send them packing. He is no sentimental Latin lover. Even middle-aged ladies from the village, who should know better, bring him home-made fruit cakes, and perch on his bony knees in the blue armchair.

Kurt laughs at Cathy's disapproving face. 'Don't watch the bungalow if what happens in there upsets you. It is not your business. This is a farm, not a Sunday school meeting.'

*

In the evenings she walks by herself in the river fields. She stands by a willow-tree and watches the turquoise mayflies dance and die on the dark brown water. The sweet, brackish river smell has a curious drawing power, and she knows that the growing child can sense it. But there are times when her fears overwhelm her, and the river walk cannot calm her. It is that old familiar terror of not fulfilling the expectations of others: of failing to measure up. Of loving, and yet knowing herself to be unloved. She grows irritable, and vents her misery on Kurt. 'Why is it you never mention the baby?' she demands. 'You talk about pigs and calves, but never a word about your child.'

'We do not have a child – we only hope. You think too much about it.'

She chooses to ignore his meaning. 'I want to decide on a name: what will go well with Baumann?'

'No,' he shouts, 'no names. You must not give name, it will be bad omen.'

She ignores him. 'If it is a girl I shall call her Emma for your aunt. If a boy, he will take your second name. Paul Baumann will sound very well.'

It soon becomes clear to her that the sight of the pram and the baby clothes upsets him and so she purposely leaves small, half-finished garments lying about, where he cannot fail to see them. She thinks she knows what his trouble is. The child is to be his stake for the future: the cure for his rootless state; and her failure to give him a living child would be all the proof he could ever need of her inadequacy. In spite of his loving ways, she is still convinced that he does not love her.

*

Cathy has hardly known what to expect. In books and films the birth is achieved by means of gallons of boiling water, and a country doctor's black bag. She knows there must be more to it than that: but has, so far, found it impossible to admit her ignorance to Kurt. His midwifery skills are concerned with cows and horses: in an emergency she might even be thankful to trust herself to him. To begin with she attributes the colicky pains around her middle to the eating of unripe apples on the previous evening.

According to a pre-arranged plan, she phones for a taxi. She will not allow Kurt to go with her: she is about important business, and as she has said before, in another place, he always makes her so bloody nervous. The hospital labels and gowns her, and leaves her alone to assess the extent of her terror: which is extreme. The Sister-in-charge, newly promoted, views her with what may well become desperation.

'I don't like the look of this one,' she mutters, 'too small, too damned tiny.'

'Do you understand what is happening Mrs Baumann?' The Sister's tone is brisk. 'Are you aware of what follows this stage of labour?'

'No: and don't bother to tell me.' She shivers and sweats, and averts her eyes from the waiting crib.

The bone crunching pain goes on forever; she does not recognise the voice that screams in an effort to birth the child. 'Nobody told me,' she cries, 'nobody said it would be like this.' And the tears of chagrin roll down her face at the thought of the hoax that has been perpetrated upon her.

After several hours, a doctor is summoned. 'Who would have thought, to look at her, that she had such strength,' they say. 'See how she goes on fighting.' The child is born into silence. Dangling blue and lifeless, upside down in the doctor's hands, she knows it is dead.

'I didn't really name it,' she whispers; they are doing terrible things to the baby, and she closes her eyes. Life is slipping from her, and she lets it go. The ennui of failure claims her.

'Watch out for the mother,' somebody shouts, 'she's haemorrhaging.' As the hypodermic pierces her thigh she thinks she can hear the baby crying.

*

No one has told her about the glory. He is brought to her in a small, blue blanket and the smiling tears of happiness slide down her face, and she is full of the glory of him. It is sweeter than falling in love; louder than music; stronger than fear; as if she had been born again, but assured and decisive this time. She has not failed.

The maternity ward is overcrowded. The beds are so close together that there is scarcely room for the nurses to pass between them. Several bored faces peer out, over magazines, but nobody speaks. It is visiting time for the fathers: they shuffle uneasily into the ward, hang-dog in the face of so many proven and fertile women. They clutch brown paper bags full of oranges and clean nighties. There are those who peek first at their offspring, and those who go first to their wives.

Cathy wonders what route Kurt will take, when he comes.

Night-Sister is middle-aged, and Irish. Her name is O'Hara.

'Hasn't your husband come in to see you darlin'?' She looks doubtfully at Cathy's wedding ring, although it is 22 carat gold.

'We live on a farm: it's a long way out of town, and we don't have a car.'

'He should be here.' She straightens the sheet with a vicious tweak.

'You've had a rough time, my girl. You and the baby. Birth cord was tight around his neck: d'ye know, he nearly strangled?'

*

The gypsy girl is brought in at midnight. The whole ward can hear the sound of her moaning, and the fear in the voice of the boy who is with her. O'Hara is wild. 'He brought her here on his motorbike, and her so far gone that she can't stand up!'

The Sister stands, hands on hips, in the middle of the ward. 'We've no bed to put her in: aren't the lot of you packed in like sardines already.'

Two nurses are fetched and instructed to move a cupboard; a bed is brought in from another ward and squeezed into the vacant space. The Sister is rushing in and out of the swinging doors like a woman demented. 'Her head's full of lice,' moans O'Hara, 'sure and isn't she lousy all over. She stinks to high heaven; the dear doctor is holding his nose.' Ten minutes later O'Hara returns, grinning broadly. 'Wouldn't ye know it me darlin's,' she tells the captive, goggle-eyed mothers, 'that gypsy baby weighs nearly ten pounds. Popped out like a hero, and looks ready to walk and talk.'

The gypsy girl is wheeled up to the corner bed. She refuses to speak and her eyes roll wildly. Her face is hostile under a matt of thick black curls. The boy has followed the stretcher in through the door. 'Only a minute now,' O'Hara warns him.

Cathy can see where the soles of his shoes are flapping loose: his feet are filthy. He is sobbing wildly, and the girl puts a tentative hand on his head. O'Hara is touched. 'No more than a pair of kids,' she sniffs into her hanky, 'jumped over the broomstick, I shouldn't wonder. Must get him away from that bed or we shall all be scratching.'

Paul Baumann is three days old when first seen by his father. There is a commotion in the corridor, and O'Hara's voice raised in anger. 'Sure and hadn't we all decided that you were fictitious?'

Kurt will visit his wife and his son in the farm's good time. He walks down the Ward looking chastened but still defiant. He does not shuffle his feet like the other fathers: or avoid the eyes of the curious mothers. He locates his wife and bends over to kiss her. Cathy thinks there are tears in his eyes, but she cannot be sure.

She feels shy with him: as if she has come back from a distant place, and he is a man she has just been introduced to. 'Do you like my baby?' she asks politely. He turns back to the crib. 'Ach Gott,' he says, 'my son. Ist das nicht wunderbar?'

Kurt is moved. He returns to the cradle again and again, as if he cannot quite believe what he sees there. Satisfaction is a feeling she has not known very often. She is longing to ask him where the hell he has been since Thursday, but for the moment, she cannot bring herself to destroy his pleasure.

At tea-time she drinks three cups of tea, and eats four jam sandwiches, to make up for lost time. Until Kurt had come, she had not felt hungry.

'Three days,' she whispers urgently, 'three days and two nights, and you haven't bothered to come and see if I am dead or alive.'

'We have trouble on Moorseek,' he interrupts, 'Sante has fall and break his arm. I must do all the work alone.'

She is almost crying, 'If you were ill I would crawl every inch of the way to be with you.'

'But you are not ill. Hospital tell me on telephone. All is OK.'

'If you really cared you would want to be here.'

He hitches his chair up close to the bed. 'I care. I am here now. What more will you have me do? I cannot leave Moorseek: it is my responsibility. There is stock to be fed and watered: cows to milk. You know about these things. You have worked on a farm.'

'The gypsy boy cared,' says Cathy, 'he stayed all the time: they couldn't make him go.' Kurt stares blankly at her for several seconds. 'I believe,' she cries, 'that you think the birth of the baby has unhinged me. I hate that farm. I hate anything and anyone that takes you away from me.'

Kurt looks uneasily at the ranks of listening mothers. 'You will feel better when you come home,' he whispers, 'you are upset, that is all.' He walks away from the bed and waves when he reaches the door. He hasn't asked if it had been a bad experience, or if she had suffered terribly. He is only accustomed to dealing with cows and horses: and they, poor things, have no choice but to suffer.

*

The arm that supports the baby has started to tremble. She is surprised at the solid weight of him: he looks so tiny among the folds of the big, white shawl. Responsibility, she thinks: my weight of responsibility; and she shifts him gently and inexpertly so that he lies across her shoulder. She sees that the stubble fields have been ploughed under: the ridged black earth curves upwards now to meet the sky. The old trees that crowd around the house have lost their leaves, and the colours of the land have altered: grown muted and sombre. The air is colder, and she walks into the house on tottery, trembling legs, and wonders what else has changed in her absence.

The house is filled with the resinous scent of burning logs. Kurt has lit fires in every room: has spared the time from his urgent duties around the farm to do so. But of course, he will want the house to be warm for the baby's sake.

*

When he looks at his child, Kurt's face becomes soft and bright with yearning: and he cannot conceal it. He wills the baby to wake and cry, so that he may lift him up and observe the miracle of him more closely. At intervals during the night, he approaches the sleeping child and shines a torch on his face to check that he still breathes. Cathy sees this vigilance as a threat, and a criticism of her ability as a mother.

Kurt writes a letter to Dresden. 'On October 4th 1949 our first son was born. His name is Paul and he is a healthy and beautiful child.' Over his shoulder, she reads the first lines, and sees a certain finality in the words he has written. They read like a declaration and she knows he will never be able to leave her now.

The baby will bind him to her for ever.

Over in Kingsbridge, Cathy's mother is saying, 'It seems to be working out all right: they seem to be happy.'

'Of course,' says her father, 'he's older than Cathy, and I don't think he has much sense of humour. But then, they don't do they? The Germans. Always been known as a race of straight-faced people.'

There are times when the Wyatts experience doubts. War has not touched them: has been no more than an inconvenience in their lives. But now, it lies like a stain across this happiness that has come to them with the birth of their first grandchild. It hardly seems fair.

Cathy's mother approves of Kurt. He calls her Mum, which she finds touching: and it helps her to love him like a son, which she has never expected to do.

Sante takes a deep interest in the baby. He hovers around the pram whenever it stands in the winter sunshine beside the kitchen door: and he speaks softly to the sleeping child and calls him 'Paulo mio.' Cathy finds this strange and says so to Kurt.

'He doesn't seem the type to be fond of babies: why hasn't he had one of his own? There are plenty of willing contenders for the honour.'

'Sante is unhappy man,' Kurt tells her, 'he has a boy in Italy, but he has not seen him since 1943.'

'But you said that he wasn't married.'

'And he is not. The mother of Sante's son will not marry with him. He writes letters and sends her money: but she will not have him as husband. He carries a picture of her and the child in that locket he wears: now perhaps you can understand why he never goes home.'

*

Winter closes in around Moorseek Farm, and Cathy is left alone in the whispering house with only the baby for company, and a growing conviction that she has no talent for being a farmer's wife. She is bored and restless, and can find no ease for her lively mind among cows and chickens. The baby presents no challenge: once bathed and fed, he sleeps until hunger wakes him.

'Life is not always sonnenschein for any of us,' Kurt tells her. 'Why do you always want what I cannot give you?'

Anger flickers between them like lightning, across the kitchen table. Usually it is harmless enough, but sometimes a strike is made, and damage is done. They are eating the meal Kurt calls 'abendbrot', which for Cathy is neither tea nor supper. She voices the grievances which have smouldered for many days: her head is aching again, and the sight of the food revolts her. 'I'm buried alive in this place: I have no one to talk to.' She pushes her plate away. 'And why do you have to get up so early? You can't see what you're doing at five in the morning.'

He frowns: 'I do not need to see. I know this place well: I would find my way without eyes.'

'But you don't need to start work so early. There's no point in being the boss if you can't sneak an extra hour in bed on a winter's morning. You don't even wait for a cup of hot coffee – what are you trying to prove with all this? That I am the one who is lazy?' She never sleeps properly once he has left her side: the bed grows cold without him in it; and the clatter of pails and the banging of cowshed doors sounds like a reproach, undermining her pleasure. The quarrel draws power from its own impulsion and deepens. 'I never wanted to come to this place, but nobody asked me: my opinions count for nothing. I was clubbed and dragged to this cave by my hair, like an ancient Briton.'

Kurt stares at her for several seconds, without blinking. 'I have never hit you,' he sounds bemused, 'or dragged you by the hair: and this is a very good house – not cave.'

'Don't be so bloody literal,' she screams, 'that was intended to be a joke. So why aren't you laughing? or don't you know how to?'

'You will have to warn me,' he shouts back, 'let me know when you are going to say something funny. How shall I know the difference, all your talk is so crazy, I never know when is time to laugh.'

She is off on another tack. 'I'm lonely. You only come back to the house when you are too tired to do anything else. This farm has become an obsession with you.'

He looks surprised. 'Of course the farm must come first. It is my duty: and duty must always come first. It is pity that you do not know your duty also.' He pushes his plate clear across the table. 'You cannot cook proper food. Every day we eat "ersatz". Spam is fit for the dogs: and I do not like this sticky white bread that you buy in the town. I bring you milk, eggs, cream, and you use a tin-opener.' He stands up abruptly: 'We will have a new order here in the kitchen. I will show you cooking the German way. We begin tomorrow.'

*

Snow blocks the lane that leads to the town. It covers the fields and fills the yard: and drifts in cotton-wool billows against the door and the windows. The whole valley is white and silent: and Cathy looks for alternatives, and cannot find one. She blows dust from her copy of Chambers Dictionary, and turns to the words that begin with H *Hausfrau*. One whose interests are bounded by the household. Root Germanic.

It seems she will have to become a Hausfrau: bounded by household interests; root Germanic. She will wear an embroidered apron, and twist her hair in a plait, and braid it around her head, like his Tante Emma. She will rise with her husband the farmer, at five every morning and brew him his coffee. She will learn how to talk about crops, and mastitis in cows, and the price of eggs.

*

Kurt demands the sort of spices and herbs that the Kingsbridge grocers have never heard of: so he writes to his mother in Dresden, and she sends him small, pungent packets wrapped up in muslin. He makes paprika goulash, eisbein-with-sauerkraut, and spiced apfel-kuchen. He teaches his English wife how to bake her own bread and churn her own butter.

'So when did you learn all this?' she demands. 'Are you sure you weren't married before you met me?'

The set of his mouth means that once again, she has gone too far.

'Joke!' she cries, 'you know that I didn't mean it.'

He spreads his fingers wide in the un-English gesture: 'As a child,' he tells her, 'I always watched my mother: I never learned anything useful from books.' It is surprising how deeply that final sentence rankles.

'We are different,' she admits, 'and it didn't seem to matter before the baby came: but now I begin to worry about it. Sometimes I think that he is all that we have in common: your blood and mine, mingled together. What does that make him? A battlefield? We never talk to each other: I mean, communicate, with understanding. We shoot words at one another, like snipers loosing off bullets. We make demands: state terms, like opposing armies. Do you know what I'm saying, Kurt? the war never ended: it's still going on, right here in our own backyard.'

His gesture negates her words: 'Ach ja! I wondered when that would come into the argument – the war – it is only a problem because you make it so. I am a man of peace –'

She interrupts him, 'When you are having things all your own way, you are very peaceful: I can vouch for that.' She lays her head against her hand: 'I'm tired of fighting with you: it makes my head ache. If only you would talk to me; trust me, the way you trust Sante. Oh yes, I know you and he have long discussions. I am shut out: it's as if twenty-eight years of your life have gone missing, and I am left to make sense of a few odd pieces.'

He is silent for several minutes. 'It is hard for me to speak with you,' he says at last, 'because you have never suffered. Because you are English you think that God is an Englishman too, and must be on your side. Sante and I start equal. He speaks my sort of language. It is the talk of outcasts, of losers: we are the men who are not allowed to be proud anymore: we must walk with the head bowed, nicht wahr? How can I talk with you Cathy? I have no voice. Only the people who win are allowed to speak: it is better that I stay silent.'

*

A warm wind blows from the south and the deep snows melt; and the valley is green again. Kurt says 'Snow does not last long in England. In Pommern it lies from November till April. The frost is hard and the lakes freeze over. When I was a boy we lit fires by the lake and had skating parties: es war eine schöne zeit!'

His words conjure up sweet pictures for her. He is admitting her, into his mind, but slowly. She enters it tentatively, and with great trepidation. Who knows what else she might find in there?

The sun comes back, and the days grow longer. The farm has an ordered, prosperous look. Black and white cattle graze peacefully over green meadows: and Kurt remembers to smile at Cathy and call her Liebling, which he has often neglected to do since coming to Moorseek. He is putting down roots, and the roots are in alien soil.

Kurt Baumann is happy: but his contentment is achieved only at the expense of others; and so he sends parcels of clothing and food to his mother and sister in Dresden, in an attempt to assuage his guilt. But the guilt remains.

Cathy wraps up the parcels in brown hessian, which is stronger and more durable than paper. She sews on labels of thick white cambric, and prints the address several times, in indelible ink. She too, parcels up her conscience with warm woollen jumpers and tins of pure coffee. What else can she do? She has stolen the only remaining man in the Baumann family.

*

In less than two years she is pregnant again: and this time it is Cathy who will not choose names: or knit white woolly garments. She is coming around to his country-boy's faith in the good and bad omens: among many other things.

The baby is born without pain, and six weeks too early; legs threshing, fists brandished; lashless blue eyes screwed tight shut. She has not suffered to give him life, and so, conversely, she cannot weep when they lay him beside her. He is an amazing replica of his father: already he has a truculent air about him; long straight nose, hard jawline.

'He's not a bit like your first,' says O'Hara.

'He gave me no trouble.'

'He's biding his time,' says O'Hara darkly, 'this little divil will break your heart. I'll put money on it.'

Kurt Baumann has learned his lesson well. He appears in the ward on time, with the rest of the fathers.

'Another boy,' Cathy tells him, 'and this one looks just like you. He keeps turning his face away: I don't think he likes me.'

Kurt rests a hand on her head and smiles, 'You are always like this when you are away from me. When you come home all will be in order.' All is not in order. Her headaches return after nine months absence: but there is no time now to cosset her queasy stomach and throbbing temples.

'Why is he always crying? Du lieber Gott what is wrong here?' Kurt as always, meets worry with anger.

'I don't know,' she says wearily, 'I can't think what to do, any more. Paul was never like this.'

The doctor is summoned. 'A perfectly healthy baby,' he declares, 'perhaps the trouble lies with the mother. Feed him on Cow and Gate: and I am sure you will see an improvement.'

A hundred times in the day she kneels down to embrace her first child. It calms her to smooth his flaxen hair and hold his small body close. Paul, it seems, is to be her only success in a lifetime of failure.

*

The winter is one of the wettest on record. The river is in full flood, and at one stage the farmhouse itself has been threatened. Supplies are being ferried across to them daily by dinghy; and the cattle brought close to the house, and penned in the yards for safety. Kurt has his problems. The baby continues to cry and lose weight.

'He'll die,' she tells Kurt, 'and it won't be my fault: he hates me. I know it. I haven't chosen a name in case it should bring bad luck.' The baby grows rigid within her grasp, and turns blue with temper.

'Take him,' she cries one evening, 'I can't stand anymore. I can't bear it.'

Kurt has never yet held this child in his arms: and she sees how his eyelids flicker in fear as she thrusts the child at him.

In his father's arms, the baby stops crying at once. Kurt picks up the bottle and begins to rock the child gently. He croons to him softly, as he would do to an orphaned calf who has had to accept a substitute mother. The baby is taking the food. His pale little face is flushed bright red from the unusual effort. As soon as the bottle is empty, he sleeps. O'Hara was right after all. She can feel her heart breaking.

Kurt names his second son Martin. It is not a family name, and there is no precedent for it. Which seems only right and proper since this is a singular child. Kurt re-arranges his whole working schedule, making sure he is always on hand for the four-hourly feeds.

The baby will agree to sleep through the night only when laid on his father's shoulder: small face tucked into Kurt's neck, like a motherless puppy.

*

Away from the kitchen of Moorseek Farm, and beyond the cliffs of Dover, events are taking place in the world, which will, one day touch the little Baumann family. But not yet.

The trials of Nuremberg are over. The Nazi leaders have been tried and sentenced: and hanged by the neck until they are properly dead. Justice is done: and is seen to be done, which is more important. But justice alone is not sufficient. There is still a whole nation to be condemned: but how can you hang a whole nation? Even though they have almost succeeded in exterminating the Jews.

Cathy wonders whether the pressure to show remorse is generated spontaneously from with the German nation, or if has been grafted onto them by the hot-gospelling politicians of another country. She reads newspaper editorials, and listens to lengthy radio discussions on the subject. The fact remains that Germany is in the grip of a fresh hysteria, and a new religion. It is known as 'collective guilt'.

Cathy comes rather late in the day to this knowledge; moving from country to country, and having babies, had hindered her in her grasp of world affairs: but she has always been good at making up for lost time.

Germany has been discredited in the eyes of the world: and the people, since 1945, have been told to atone for their sins, and to be seen to do so, as publicly, and as often as possible. They have been encouraged if not actually commanded, to beat their breasts and confess to sins which they may or may not have committed. Cathy sees danger in this. Surely, the truly evil men are the ones who will never confess: so what of the others? It must, she thinks, have been difficult to experience a 'communal shame' along with an empty firegrate, and an empty belly. But the people, being German and therefore obedient and conditioned to taking orders, seem to achieve a ragged salvation by way of their new religion: and, who knows, perhaps they are wise to do so.

No one has told Kurt Baumann that he is expected to suffer 'collective guilt' in common with his fellow countrymen in the Fatherland. Such an expression has never penetrated as far as Moorseek, except in the newspapers read by Cathy; and even if it had come to his notice, he would not have found it impressive. Kurt has a method of dealing with disquieting information, which is dangerous and unwise, but characteristic. He turns his back:

because that has always been his way of dealing with life's unacceptable truths.

*

The fortnightly letter from Dresden is bulkier than usual. It holds eight pages of closely written script and contains two statements which Cathy finds equally shocking.

A relative called Tante Marie has hanged herself from a hook on her bedroom door; and Kurt's mother proposes a meeting with her son and his wife in the coming April.

'Who is Tante Marie?' asks Cathy.

'The youngest sister of my mother.'

'Why has she hanged herself. I don't understand your sister's letter. She says that your aunt became too religious, and allowed certain things to prey on her mind. What things?'

Kurt lips compress to the hard white line that means anger. He folds the pages carefully, and inserts them into the envelope as if he can file away his distress and confusion. 'We will not speak of this matter. My aunt has shamed us.'

'Shamed you? How can you be so unfeeling? That poor woman: imagine how desperate she must have been. To wait for the house to be empty and all of them gone to church on a Sunday evening, and then to loop a dressing-gown cord around her neck – it's a tragedy Kurt!'

He gets up from the breakfast table, pulls on his jacket and takes a few steps to the door. Over his shoulder he mutters, 'I must go. I have work to do. We are drilling wheat this morning: and the vet will be here at ten to give an injection. We shall need coffee. Those two calves that were born last night – can you enter them up in the Herd Book for me?'

Cathy says, 'What are you talking about? Coffee – Herd Book: have you gone crazy? This is important Kurt. I want to talk about it: and I'm not so impressed by your passion for work any more. It usually means that you want to avoid an issue.'

He moves slowly away from the door, and back towards her. He picks up the letter and uses it to stab at the space between them. 'So there are things you would like to know,' he says quietly, 'but have you the stomach for what I will tell you?'

Sudden fear makes her flippant. 'Fire away,' she cries, 'I can take it.'

'All right,' he says, 'sit down, and I will tell you all about German women: especially the ones in my family. They were all raped in 1945. Not once or twice, but many times: some to the very point of dying. This was done by the Russians. Mongols. Drunken men who were worse than animals. No animal ever behaved as they did. That was one thing. Their husbands are lost; no letter, no last goodbye, no grave to visit. That is another sorrow. Their homes and land have been taken from them. Our village is Polish territory now: that is like amputation for people like us. We have lost the good earth that gave us birth.' He strikes a heavy blow on the table. 'These women have lost all they had, and still they must find a way to go on living. The one who has killed herself has betrayed them: she has not kept faith: she is traitor. No one has the right to his own self-murder.'

Cathy says, 'It was true then, those stories we heard on the train from Berlin. I didn't believe that girl – that Inge. I thought she was making it up, to make herself seem important.'

The look he gives her pierces her right to the bone. He shakes his head sadly. 'You,' he says, 'I am afraid that you too are the sort of woman who would hang herself on a hook. You would not find the courage to go on living would you?'

Cathy tries to visualise rape, and fails. After all, she has only known gentleness and love. She tries to imagine widowhood and the loss of her home; and having to feel a 'communal shame' because she is English.

He is right: they must never discuss this matter again.

*

They are hoeing the sugar-beet: a backbreaking job disliked by both men. Sante straightens his aching back and looks sternly at Kurt. 'You are leetle bits hard on your wife, sometimes, camparo. She is English girl remember. They do not have the fire and the toughness of your women and mine.' He rocks his palm to and fro, 'They are leetle bit so-so these English.'

Kurt frowns and is silent. He talks about most things with Sante, but Cathy is private.

'I speak of the heart,' grins Sante, 'you have to make a woman believe that you cannot live without her: that is the secret.'

'A woman must have a man. That is true,' Kurt says, 'but a man stands alone. His is the master: he does not depend on a woman.'

'You are a strong man now,' says Sante, 'but when you are old and sick what will you do? Look at me camparo! already I come to the middle-age, and I have no loving woman to lean on.'

'Sick? me, sick? I do not even catch cold,' Kurt taps his forehead. 'Illness is all in the head. If you have work to do, you will have no time for such fancies.'

*

The concrete yard is enclosed by high white gates, and the cowshed doors are kept closed, on Cathy's orders. Paul Baumann rests his forehead against the rough white slat and the wood feels warm on his skin: between the gaps, he can see the green river fields and the willows. He gives the gates an experimental shake, but he knows that they will not part. His mother has fastened them with a padlock.

Last year, when he had been only three years old, the gates had stood open. The tractors had roared in and out, unimpeded, and Paul had made several small sorties out into the meadow: but never too far. He never goes into the cowsheds: the noise and the bustle upset him; Paul at the age of four, is a solitary child.

Papa has a name for each cow. He talks to them in his German words, as if they are people. Sante also talks to the cows, but he speaks in a different language. Paul knows that Papa and Sante are different. It is only his mother and grandparents, and the milk-lorry driver who speak proper English.

He had only gone into the field for a minute, to pick daisies: but the thought of the ladysmocks had drawn him away to the dip in the meadow where the willow trees grew. Ladysmocks were special. Papa had said that they only flowered in the marshy hollows. It was while he was kneeling to pick them that he first smelled it; a funny, rotting, pleasing smell that made him forget that he was so far from the farmhouse. He had seen the river several times before when riding the horse with Papa or sitting on Sante's shoulder. 'You not come to this place by yourself, Paulo mio,' Sante had warned him, 'river is very deep: maybe you fall in and drown.' But he had forced his way through the hedge that day, and the dark brown river had reached out and claimed him: he had sat down on the bank and dangled his feet in the water. He'd trailed his hand and made ripples: in the end he had fallen asleep on the grassy edge. The long walk had tired him.

His mother had cried when she found him; he had said that the ladysmocks were for her, but that only made her cry harder. Papa had been angry with her. 'He is all right. Nothing bad has happened. He is a boy and all boys have to leave their mothers sometimes; you must learn to expect it.' Paul lifts his head from the wooden slat; he kicks at the high white gate, and shakes it. The padlock rattles. He can just see the dip in the field where the willow trees grow. He can feel the tug of the river right down to the soles of his sandals.

He will escape from them all, one day. When no one is watching.

*

Martin crosses the yard on fat, unsteady legs. He can hear his father's voice and the pump of machines; the cows have come in for milking. He bangs on the cowshed door with a sticky fist, but nobody hears him, and so he begins to scream.

His father comes running. Martin is grabbed and lifted up and over the half-door. 'Ach du,' scolds Papa, 'you must not come here. Mama will be angry.' Martin opens his throat for another scream. 'Las ruhig sein,' Papa whispers. He carries Martin into the shed and places him high on a stack of hay bales. 'Sit there, and if you are good boy, I let you stay by me.'

Martin only wants to be with Papa and the cows. He loves the sheds, and the warn sweet smells that can sooth and please him; but he knows that, as always, his pleasure will be short lived.

She has to come running almost at once. He can see the swing of her long red hair, and the angry pink in her face. 'Kurt' she cries out 'where is Martin? I know he is with you. Will you please hand him over.'

Martin would like to hide in the hay: he wriggles and burrows, and covers his face with his hands. He can feel the anger rise into his throat, and he knows he will scream and bite if she takes him.

'No,' he shouts, then 'nein', then 'niente': they are the best words he knows in any language, but it makes no difference. He is handed back, as he always is, to his mother. Papa has whispered again, before handing him over 'Not cry schnuki. I fetch you later. Only go now with Mama.'

Martin feels better at once. He smiles as he sinks his front teeth in his mother's shoulder. Why can she not understand that he only wants to be with Papa, and the cows?

Part Five

1979

The express gathered speed as they drew away from Neue Braunschweig and Catherine Baumann began to feel apprehensive at the thought of the East German border. 'My mother-in-law didn't like me,' she said. It was an involuntary statement: she had never before in all her life made that particular admission.

Jürgen Hecht laughed. 'Mine would have murdered me, if she'd dared to.'

'No,' said Cathy thoughtfully, 'it wasn't like that. It went deeper. I suppose I expected too much. I have always had this desperate need for people to like me; but I had stolen their son and brother: they were justified in feeling a certain amount of resentment towards me.'

'German people,' said Jürgen, 'were in a curious frame of mind in the early 1950s. For years, we had seen ourselves as kings of the castle: and then, all at once, we were the naughty rascals. The villains of Europe; the whole world in fact. Our "economic miracle" was yet to happen. We were totally demoralised for many years: there were a great many suicides at that time, and no wonder.' He paused: 'Do you have any children?'

'Two,' she replied, 'two sons: both married now, with children of their own.' She sighed, 'I hope they will make wiser parents than I did. It wasn't enough for me to aspire to being a German-style Hausfrau, I wanted to be the perfect mother. I failed of course – well I had to – I wasn't equipped; and no one achieves that miracle anyway. I can see that now.' She moved uneasily in her seat, 'I am always so conscious of failure,' she said.

They have a couple of good years, in which Kurt's own sows farrow-down with heavy litters, and his hens lay their eggs like clockwork. She discovers that he has withdrawn a substantial amount of cash from the bank. Money which, Cathy thinks, could not have been saved without a certain degree of self-sacrifice on her part. 'I thought you were saving up to buy land,' she taunts him, 'when I wanted a new winter coat you said it would have to wait until next year. All that money blued on hotels and tickets! This trip to Dietkirchendorf must be very important?'

He explains: 'My mother has had an illness: her heart is damaged. She is to travel to Dietkirchendorf and spend some time with my Tante Emma. She would like us to meet her there.'

Frau Baumann's letters are written in the old-fashioned German script that Cathy has never been able to decipher. The unbreakable family code: she calls it. So, Kurt has not thought it necessary to tell her about his mother's illness; once again he has bitten on the bullet: hugged the open blade to his chest. She is convinced that the news he has not seen fit to divulge will, as usual, turn out to be the most significant, in the long run.

*

April 23rd 1953, and the weather in England is mild and spring-like. In Dietkirchendorf, Lower Saxony, it is still winter. Icy winds corkscrew in and out of the twisted Rapunzel houses, and patches of sullen snow lie out on the hills.

Cathy recalls the 'Schweizerhaus' as being a grim-looking hostel for refugee workers. Fresh paint and new curtains have worked wonders, the owner tells her; it is almost, but not quite, the pleasant small hotel it had been before 1940. That night they sleep in hand-carved beds under white feather-duvets.

Frau Baumann and her daughter Christina are due to arrive on the following morning.

They come together awkwardly on the station platform: kissing and clasping hands, hunting for words that will bridge the gap of their long separation. Cathy, with an awed and silent child on either hand, stands by, as her husband tries out his role of prodigal son, and brother. She suspects that he has forgotten his lines: or perhaps he has never known them. Or can it be that he knows too well what is expected of him? Cathy's limited German keeps her hovering uncertainly on the edge of the magic circle. Oh, they are polite! They try to include her. She understands all they are saying, but cannot reply. What a pity! She has rarely seen Kurt at a disadvantage, but his sure touch has deserted him now. Crossed lines have made him slow footed.

Embarrassment over his tongue-tied wife is mixed with an over-weening pride in his two small sons. He revolves uneasily among them: now speaking English, then German: and frequently mixing both languages together.

Poor Kurt. His female relatives seem to have overwhelmed him.

*

The hotel lounge overlooks the garden. Precise rows of cold yellow tulips are set in square beds, and dip low in a stiff east wind. Out in the hills she can see people climbing. The hill-walkers and tourists are finding their way once again to the Weserbergland. Trees have been planted; hotels re-opened. The bad old days of war have been put in their place, and set firmly behind them. Or have they?

Cathy thinks that Kurt's mother, still shrouded in widow's grey, has been keeping the ashes of conflict lukewarm, at least. Reproach comes in various guises. The first sight of her mother-in-law, on the station platform, has triggered a flood of unwilling repentance in Cathy. So what does she really owe this grey woman? A son – or nothing? The very words that describe Frau Baumann's condition are loaded.

Refugee. War-widow. Heart-attack victim. She draws up compunction without any effort. Her state of health is precarious: she walks slowly, leaning heavily on Kurt's arm. This journey has been taken against her doctor's advice. A calculated risk.

Cathy, resentful and frequently close to tears these days, knows very well that Frau Baumann deserves her love: and she would truly like to oblige her – but cannot.

*

Christina, who closely resembles Kurt, is a blonde and handsome woman. She had been married once, in 1940. A holiday wedding, hardly real, barely remembered any more. Ernst Leuchner had gone, with a million others, to be a soldier; had never returned from Russia. Is reported missing, but not officially dead; which leaves poor Christina neither a wife nor a widow.

The Baumanns, when gathered in private, speak the dialect of Pommern: which is oddly closer to English than the conventional 'hoch Deutsche'. They talk over the old days in Mechtenhausen. They reminisce, Cathy thinks, as the fallen angels must often have done, after their expulsion from Paradise. Girls' names drop into the conversation. Sturdy, lusty Brunhildes! these maidens of Pommern must have been. Cathy, slim as a willow: red-haired and insubstantial, is referred to disparagingly as doll-like by Kurt's mother.

Cathy would like to avoid the hotel lounge in the evenings. Without her children for camouflage she is exposed. Kurt is solicitous with his mother, as he has never once been with Cathy. She has never yet known him to be remorseful, but every gesture that he makes in his mother's presence is weighted down with contrition.

'Come: sit by the stove Mama. It is colder than ever this evening.'

'Your children should wear warmer clothing Kurt. Those little white socks are fit only for summer.'

'It is much milder in England, Mama. The cows often winter outside – in the fields. We had not thought to find snow here in April.'

Bad mark for you Cathy! Your children run unprotected in Germany's bitter winds.

'You have several grey hairs already, son,' his mother touches Kurt's temple, 'how old are you now – only thirty-two?'

Cathy has failed to observe his rapidly silvering hair: but his Mama has tracked it down; as she discovers the holes in his socks, and his missing shirt buttons. Feckless Cathy. Already marked down as a reader of obscure books, and a lover of highbrow music. Last chance, Cathy: and now you've blown it.

*

She imagines that they are showing a smooth face, at least, to his family. It had become habitual: this trick of the one-cornered smile, bent head; the easy deference she offers him in place of her anger.

If she should ever open her mouth and roar aloud her frustration and pain, she is convinced that the world would shatter. Cathy plays the game that has worked for her since childhood: she remembers St Paul on the road to Damascus, and becomes the 'softly, softly' expert. But Hedwig Baumann sees through her.

'Is Cathy not happy with you Kurt?' Cathy overhears the remark as she enters the room and, whichever way she transposes the German, the words have the same old meaning.

Cathy has Kurt and Paul and Martin for loving. She has parents, and home and England. How then dared she not be happy?

It is finally over. Nobody says so, or needs to. They all know that this is to be their last meeting, in life. Grey faced and grim, Kurt makes great play with the stowing of luggage. He settles the children with books and crayons. Prays for the whistle to blow, and end it. In spite of the promise she made him at Hobart's: once again, they are leaving his country.

*

The good years for Cathy Baumann are to be the ones in which nothing much happens. Quiet days and months are like sound apples which will keep their flavour until apples come round again.

Her life is controlled by the seasons. Her migraine attacks return with the sunlight in springtime, and retreat with the first frosts of autumn. She hides in dark corners, and fears she is cheating her husband. A German wife would have worked by his side in the fields: would have earned that desirable title of 'kameradin'.

But Cathy is fragile and doll-like. Hedwig Baumann had said

so. Kurt is all sunshine, all warmth, and she is unable to match him. She is the promising bud that is never to open. Her milieu is shadow. Increasingly, she is aware of her debt to him. Without him she would have withered and fallen already: whatever she knows of life and love, she owes to Kurt Baumann. Gratitude makes her slavish. 'I love you,' she tells him; and means it. Cathy having reached her thirty-third birthday, is gradually growing into the kind of woman she thinks she should have been at the age of twenty. She is aware of changes within herself and wonders why it has taken so long to achieve them. Belated recognition of what she has makes her careful of it. She becomes obsessed by the need for protection; she will build stockades and hedge her bets: take out insurance. The cost of all this has yet to be calculated, but Paul and Martin are growing up in freedom, in England: and that fact alone has to count for something.

It can even, if she works hard at it, be sufficient justification for all of her past and future actions.

*

The sun comes into the kitchen on summer mornings. On a clean, checked tablecloth, a home-bred, home-cured ham sits between the loaf she has baked, and the pot of jam made from last year's blackberries (picked by her purple-tongued, lip-stained boys). Breakfast is always at 8 a.m. After milking, says Paul.

Cathy twists a knob, and the radio, muttering away to itself on the shelf, speaks up loud and clear.

June 17th 1953: and the people of East Berlin are rising against their Russian masters. Communist Party offices have been forcibly entered and records and documents thrown into the streets and set fire to. Gaols have been invaded, and prisoners released. Workers have attacked Russian tanks with sticks and paving stones. Armoured vehicles have been overturned and burned. The trouble is spreading rapidly to other towns and cities in East Germany. People are being killed and injured. Kurt's face, across the oasis of the breakfast table, is growing pinched, and blue around the nostrils. We have lived until now, she thinks, like thieves, stealing a little comfort from one another. But out there, where he is, in the wilderness; nothing can help him.

There are a few quiet, apple-flavoured years still to be enjoyed. But not many.

East Germany begins to take up space in the newspapers, and on the radio. There is talk of hot war and cold war. Cathy's mother reminds her, incessantly, that Germans residing in England, have been either interned or sent back to their country of origin, at the start of the Second World War. The word on her mother's lips is naturalisation.

Subsequent letters from Dresden make no mention of recent upheavals. The envelopes have been opened, the contents examined, before despatch to Kurt Baumann in England.

'I am a German,' Kurt protests to Cathy, 'every pore, every cell, every drop of blood. I will not swear on the Bible to be your Queen's true man. I never did that much for Adolf Hitler.'

'You don't have to mean it,' she says. If she dared, she would hold his hand: lead him blindfold towards capitulation: 'It's a formality only: a piece of paper.'

'With my hand resting on the Holy Bible?'

*

A year later she finds his Certificate of Naturalisation thrust away in a kitchen drawer, among old receipts for cattle-feed and egg sales. It should have been framed in gold, along with the dark-blue British Passport he now possesses. But safety and normality are not to be gained by these slips of pasteboard: no matter how desperately Cathy schemes and manoeuvres.

*

Paul Baumann, aged twelve, props his bicycle carelessly up against the dairy wall. He grabs up his fishing tackle and heads for the river bank, without bothering to change out of his good school clothing. Too much fuss is made in his family about cleanliness and well-polished shoes. Paul believes he is the only one who has his priorities in the right order. Martin Baumann enters the house by the back door. He stamps his feet defiantly on the bedroom carpet. 'She' insists that mud-caked shoes be removed in the porch: and so he removes them. At this stage he is more obedient than his elder brother.

'Where's my father?' he asks as he runs through the kitchen. It is his customary greeting to his mother, and she expects no other. Martin is small for his age, but wiry. He fights all the other boys in his class: nobody bests him. His brother has said that fighting proves nothing. Paul gets all his best lines from his mother.

*

The fortnightly letters continue to come from Dresden. Christina obliges by writing hers in a script that Cathy can understand. The latest is dated August 1st 1961.

'Mama,' writes Christina, 'has suffered a massive heart attack. She is in the city hospital, and her condition is critical. I think you should come, and quickly.'

Cathy says, 'I won't let you go alone. If you go into the East we shall all go with you.' The brave gesture, like the parcels of good bean-coffee, has been made to ease her elastic conscience. Haven't they always had a tacit agreement about such deceptions? They both practise them in their separate ways. But Kurt it seems has forgotten the rules of the game. He leans on the kitchen table, body suddenly slack, eyes empty. He carefully lays down the single page of writing. 'Yes,' he says quietly, 'we must all be together. You must phone to the East German Embassy for visas.'

*

It is not often that life's little ironies will contrive to arrange themselves so neatly. The visas arrive with suspicious promptness and the four squares of bright pink pasteboard lie together beside the yellow telegram form on the breakfast table. The message from Dresden is simple. 'Mama fell asleep on the tenth of August.'

Kurt has seated himself abruptly, on a straight backed kitchen chair, and so he is obliged to meet his grief poker-spined. Compassion drives her towards him. He feels dense, and wooden to the touch: quite unlike himself. A thin, high keening noise is ripped from his throat: it is not weeping, this note is atavistic. His face is empty: the combination of blankness and anguished sound is weird, it repels her. Her arms fall away from his shoulders: she will not dare to approach him again. She goes back to clearing the breakfast table. If she takes no notice, perhaps the terrible sound he is making will stop.

The keening noise is to be preferred to the absence of voice that follows. He does not speak in the house: not even to Martin. The men who work with him and for him are given monosyllabic instructions and left to fulfil them. They respect his mood, aware of its nature. Cathy, who depends from day to day on her husband's approval, is hurled into the abyss alongside him.

She telephones Interflora and instructs that a wreath of white roses be delivered to Christina's address in Dresden. Although she cannot know it, this arrangement is made just in time. Within the week this merciful service to mourning families will no longer exist in the DDR. She tries to tell Kurt about the white roses, and the telegram of condolence despatched to Christina, but his dissenting gesture freezes her throat. If he will not speak, neither will he listen. The channels of normal communication close down between them. He is seeking for someone to blame, and she fears that she is his target. In adverse ratio the boys grow louder. They shout and push and bicker, to fill the blind corners of the mourning house.

Cathy has never experienced grief: every link in her family chain is intact. Frau Baumann's death continues to lie like a judgement on her. Dramatic events in the Baumann family are inextricably meshed with the fate of the East German people, who are also imprisoned within a divided house. On the day of Frau Baumann's funeral the last loopholes are closed in Berlin, and the two halves of that unhappy city are neatly severed.

This time the Baumanns will see events as they happen. The radio on the kitchen shelf has been supplemented by television. All U-bahn and S-bahn links in Berlin are cut; street barricades are erected; all intersections are guarded by armed police. In the Potsdamer Platz a six foot high wall of concrete springs up, overnight. Refugees are jumping from windows on the Bernauer Strasse, in a bid to escape to the West.

West Berliners turn out in their thousands, to demonstrate in front of the Brandenburg Gate, and are promptly dispersed by tear-gas and water cannon.

The division of Germany is complete. There is even a Wall to prove it.

*

Paul and Martin begin to absorb the mood of the house, and they also fall silent. It is for her children's sake that she finally tackles her husband.

'How much longer do you intend to go on with this Kurt? you are making life hard for us all. I don't think we can bear it much longer.'

He walks away from the house, and is absent for several hours. When he returns he is smiling. The problem of his grief, it would appear, has been overcome. Or has it?

*

Paul and Martin watch television. Cowboy films are favourites. Heroes are dressed in white, villains wear black. Simple logic. War films are also presented with equal fairness. The British win and the Germans lose. Well, somebody has to! Don't they?

But it is not quite real to them: that world in the square wooden box in the corner. They do not equate the brutal-faced Germans who shout Sieg Heil! and Achtung! with the loving father who wore the same uniform once, long ago. (He has photos to prove it.)

In the history class it is different. There is no background music: no well-rehearsed, slapstick drama, with 'goodies' winning, and 'baddies' losing. The history master presents them with facts.

No matter how many noses Martin punches on his way home from school that day, he will never forget the pictures he saw in the classroom. He tries to talk to his brother: but Paul, when it suits him, has blind and deaf areas of reception. This is one of them.

He finds his father down in the river meadows: his Dad, he has noticed spends most of his time alone, since German grandmama died. The hot summer's day is cooling. At Martin's approach the sheep dogs roll over ecstatically under the willow trees.

'Na boy! Where have you been? I missed you at supper.'

Martin knows, has always known, that he is his father's beloved child.

'You have something to tell me Martin?'

He can feel the words spewing up from his churning stomach. They gag in his throat, and fill his mouth. He thinks that his heart must burst: but the words will not be held back.

'Why,' he implores, 'why Belsen? Why Auschwitz, Ravensbruch, Dachau?' Is that his voice, that thin high mewling? That child's lament? He pitches his tone several octaves lower. 'Forget it Dad. It's not that important. I don't know why I asked you.'

The answer comes slowly, dragged from a hidden place. 'For some men there might have been reasons: circumstances, threats, fears for their families' safety if they did not obey the SS. I don't know what was happening in my country. I was a sailor, and then a prisoner-of-war. I only know what you know: what the pictures tell us.'

They walk home through the darkening fields. A boy with a flailing stick. A man with his dogs.

But the unspeakable words have been spoken; the question asked; and it is, after all, the beloved child who has broken the unwritten law of the family.

*

'He asked about concentration camps.'

She looks up from her book, coming back to the world he lives in. 'Who? Who asked you?'

'Martin. He wants to know how Germans could do such things.'

'And what did you tell him?'

'I said that I didn't know. That sometimes men had to act under orders.'

'You believe that do you?'

'I don't know any more.'

'You told me once that the concentration camps were a hoax, by the British Army to discredit your nation. Have you changed your mind?'

'What does it matter, what I believe or don't believe. I want to forget it. It's always "the mind" with you Cathy. Make it up:

change it. You don't live in the real world, do you? You never look at the morning fields or the sky at evening. You hide in the house when you could feel the wind on your face.' He picks up the book she has just laid down. *The Second World War*, Winston Churchill.

'This is your doing, you know. My son would not poke and probe in the past but for your example.

'I have never mentioned the war to the children. You know that.'

'It is not what is said that counts. You have an attitude Cathy. A way of not saying .'

'Martin has hurt you. He has done what I never dared to. But perhaps it is what is needed: maybe we should all sit down and discuss it together?'

'There is also the matter of Paul.' There are tears in Kurt's eyes.

'What about him?'

'He looks at me with contempt, these days. He openly disobeys me.'

She sighs. 'Paul has reached an age where he has to disobey sometimes. I get it too, you know.'

'No. I will not believe this. You love Paul too much: you spoil him. We are a family divided.'

Well, she had never expected it to be easy. Love is not always enough, it seems, not even for Martin; and Paul? What does he think about, while he plays for the wily old pike in the river shallows?

*

She finds it confusing that he does not mind talking about the war to his barber: an old RAF ace who flew hundreds of sorties over Berlin. She is never quite sure which part of him hurts, or for what reason.

Part Six

1979

'Bigotry,' said Jürgen Hecht, 'flourishes on both sides of the Channel. Down at my local they say "Evening Jürgen: what will it be then?" Behind my back they refer to me as "that Jerry who keeps the restaurant." They resent my presence among them. I also want people to like me: I too ask for more than I have any right to expect. I don't admit this to many people, but my father was a prominent Nazi. He did his ten years in Spandau, and was set free to make another fortune. Because of him I left Germany. Don't let anyone tell you that the wicked don't flourish.'

'I know a man in England,' said Catherine, 'who is full of hatred. He was too young to be in the war, but these are often the ones who nurse an undying hatred of Germans. This man's intolerance is not limited though: he also detests black people and Marxists: he is a prey to whatever prejudice happens to be in vogue at the moment. It is possible to predict with accuracy whatever his views are likely to be on any given subject. He is in shackles: more of a prisoner than those people he professes to despise.'

'You sound exactly like my wife,' said Jürgen, 'she believes in brotherly love and pacifism: but it just isn't possible to like everybody.'

Cathy smiled. 'I know,' she said, 'I'm pretty good on theory. Solitary people become very theoretical, you know. I reserve the right to dislike other people, while expecting them to like me. Kurt always said I was the most illogical person he had ever known.'

The obstacles between them have grown up slowly: but they are there. Kurt has Moorseek. He needs his preoccupations with cattle, crops, the weather. They are his old, familiar antidotes for unacknowledged miseries. What would he do without them?

He also has Martin, who displays the prominent Baumann nose, and temper, and whose fierce loyalty to minority causes is also disturbing Cathy. He would like to have Paul, for comfort, but his first-born son is elusive: has taken too much from his English mother. Paul, like his beloved element water, will always slip through his father's fingers.

*

House has become her citadel: scene of her solitary triumphs. Her carpets are vacuumed daily; her paintwork shines. She gives concentrated attention to infinitesimal detail; cannot sleep when re-decorating a room; agonises over the exact shade of curtain, or shape of cushion.

Cathy knits for her menfolk; they have more scarves, socks, sweaters than they will ever wear out in one lifetime. She will never learn how to sew: but her baking would delight Hedwig Baumann, that paragon among Hausfrauen, had she been spared to witness these latter-day victories of her English daughter-in-law. Perfection in all things domestic becomes Cathy's watchword. Nose to the grindstone; foot on the treadmill; hand to the wheel: she is a living, breathing cliché. She even attempts new skills: learns how to put paint onto door frames and windows; wields a nifty screwdriver. She listens to soap-opera radio while ironing shirts. Her books gather dust on inaccessible shelving. 'Kultur' has got the boot on Moorseek. Cathy, at last, is about the practical business of living. Her hands show a permanent cut or blister.

The bad news arrives, as ever, by post and at breakfast. Captain Penrose is dead. A car crash; death instantaneous. We regret to inform you. The heir is a nephew who practises law in London; he believes that the English Midlands is populated by savages: has actually been heard to say so. 'They hunt the fox up there, you know, and hold cock-fights down deserted mine-shafts.' Moorseek Farm will be sold to a firm of speculative builders. Mr Baumann is thanked for his years of loyal service; compensated for this abrupt termination of his employment: please find substantial cheque enclosed.

Kurt reads the letter through twice without saying a word. He ignores the cheque. For Cathy, the letter reads like a newly printed prospectus for Paradise. The cheque is substantial. She is sad about Captain Penrose. They must vacate the house by Michaelmas: the 29th day of September. 'Now we can buy a house in Kingsbridge,' says Cathy, 'and begin to live like civilised people.'

*

It rains all the time; in the years to come she will always remember those echoing houses she viewed in the deluge. Sometimes, Kurt even goes with her; he looks at the miniscule flower-beds and pocket-sized lawns; sees the smirking gnomes eternally fishing in rock-pools.

'What do you think?' she asks.

'Whatever you want: I will leave it to you.'

He is as circumspect and restrained as she could ever have wished him to be. He speaks quietly now, as if in rehearsal for his altered role in life. He has lost that old swagger: his nautical, swashbuckling air has vanished, forever. There are days when she hardly knows him. He grieves, as he had done once before, at the death of his mother. Cathy resorts to rationalisation; a rigid nature like Kurt's will take time to adjust to the faster pace of the town; and she owes it to Paul and Martin to get them away from the lonely life of the country. For seventeen years she has measured her step to her husband's rhythm. Now let it be her turn. She has fears that he might try to resurrect that old dream he once had of owning land. If that should happen, she is not quite sure of her own reaction. So easily are women convinced of their own high motives; so lightly is treachery indulged in. Kurt has been silent all evening: has actually watched television. At two o'clock in the morning she wakes to find him gripping her arm. In the lamplight she sees that his face is the colour of old tallow candles, and she is pierced through with acute and awful terror. She knows at once, that he is mortally ill.

'My chest,' he moans, 'such pain in my chest, I have my mother's sickness.'

She watches the doctor: he sits anyhow on the edge of the bed, he is creasing her white silk bedspread. His mud-caked shoes have left prints on her pale blue carpet.

Don't look at the hypodermic thrust up to the hilt in your husband's chest; don't watch the blood-pressure gauge and the doctor's fingers; only measure your fears and alarms in terms of a bedspread crumpled, a carpet stained.

The stretcher gets stuck on a bend in the narrow staircase: Kurt bites his lips, and a trickle of blood runs down his chin. The ambulance men apologise for the clumsiness that is not their fault. Horror piles up on toppling horror.

She is told to wait in a corridor in the Kingsbridge hospital. She looks down at her odd assortment of garments and puts a hand to her unbrushed hair. She drinks hot tea that the nurses bring her: and old Bible quotations float up to haunt her. 'They have taken away my Lord and I know not where they have laid him.' The doctor is speaking: 'We have put Mr Baumann into a side-ward, he will need to be quiet. He has suffered a coronary thrombosis. His blood pressure is low but stable, and we have every hope –'

'What,' she asks, 'is a coronary thrombosis?'

'His heart,' is the explanation, 'a clot, a blockage –' She has ceased to listen. His heart. That part of him, the existence of which she has always, laughingly, denied. 'It's a stone you have in there,' she has said, tapping his chest, 'stony-hearted Kurt.' She is bustled out of the hospital, 'Come back this evening,' they tell her, 'nothing that you can do now Mrs Baumann.'

The morning sky, above the hospital rooftop, is the delicate pink of a sugared almond. 'Hope cometh with the morning,' she mutters madly. You never see the morning sky, Kurt had said to her once. Well, she is looking at it now.

*

Later that day she assembles a bucket of hot soapy water, a cloth, the Hoover, and carries them up to the bedroom. The doctor's dark footprints must be expunged. The first thing she sees when she opens the door is the small, sad heap of his clothes on the wicker stool: trouser creases neatly aligned, shirt carefully folded. His wristwatch and comb lie on the dressing-table. She flings herself down on the creased white bedspread and weeps herself blind.

Downstairs, face washed, she drinks coffee, hunched up in the old armchair, in the kitchen. Paul appears, dressed for fishing. 'What's up Mum?'

'Your father,' she says, surprised: she had forgotten about her sons' existence. 'He had a heart-attack in the night. He's in hospital, in Kingsbridge.'

'How bad is it?'

'It's bad. Very bad.' She begins to cry: finds it is easy to do so, once started. Paul puts an awkward arm round her shoulders, although they are not a family accustomed to touching. 'Don't cry,' he says, 'you still have me.' Paul, whose mind, at the age of sixteen, is a total and utter mystery to her; whose hostility and reserve has frequently been directed towards her, is the one who is offering her comfort now. She will lean, for a moment, on him.

'I can talk to you Paul, because you are older than Martin. We will not tell him just yet how serious things are with your father.'

She cannot face telling Martin. Not that first day. That first Sunday.

*

The visiting hour is from six until seven: she arrives ten minutes early, and sits on a bench near the Ward Sister's office. A young nurse appears and beckons her in. The Sister pauses, assessing this frail woman's tolerance for bad news. 'Your husband is not so well this evening. He's had a small setback.'

'But,' blurts Cathy, 'he's already had a heart-attack. What else can happen to him?'

'There are complications Mrs Baumann. The next twelve hours will be crucial. You may see him for a few minutes, but you must not speak.'

A nurse, on a hard wooden chair, keeps watch at his bedside. He is lying almost flat now; head on a single pillow. He looks up, without recognition, eyes scarlet-rimmed in the sickening grey of his face. Wires from a large machine are attached to his chest with sticking plaster, and his hand has sprouted a tube which snakes upwards and into a bottle of fluid. She backs away from the bed.

'What have you done to him?' she whispers to the Sister. The left side of Kurt's face is twisted grotesquely downwards, as if half of his features have come adrift, and mistaken their point of gravity.

The Sister propels her from the room. Out in the corridor she admits, 'Well, he has had a slight stroke. In fact he is very,' she pauses, 'gravely ill. We are waiting for a specialist to come out from Leicester. Mr Williams is an excellent man. He will do all he can.'

'Can I stay here?'

'Come back later this evening Mrs Baumann. Your presence here can serve no good purpose. There is nothing you can usefully do.'

*

The thinking part of her mind has ceased to function. In other circumstances, it has been possible to ease tension by polishing the furniture, or tackling a pile of washing. She wanders into the fading light of the August evening, and heads instinctively for the road that leads out to her parents' house.

The church has always stood on the corner, but she has never halted beside the broad oak door. On this night she grasps the heavy iron ring, and the weight of the door pulls her inwards. A strip of blue carpet leads up to the altar; a few candles illuminate a Crucifix; a fat brass bowl holds pink roses. She kneels down on a lumpy red hassock, because it seems the correct thing to do. She places her hands together, very precisely, matching finger to finger.

Hypocrite; charlatan; thief. To come into this place out of need. There's no truth in that. No value. God is not a British officer in Hanover. He will not laugh and put the world to rights at her request. She has no credit in this bank: her account is empty.

Then bargain. Make God a good offer: one that he can't refuse.

Eh God. What about it then! Are you on?

She lays herself down, deliberately prostrate, before the altar rails, on the dusty blue carpet. She cries out, 'God. Jesus. Moses. Can you hear me? My life for his then – fair exchange?' Nothing happens. She gets to her feet and brushes the dust from her navy blue skirt. She smooths her hair and wipes her face; nothing has changed. Nor will it.

'Have you eaten?' her father asks. Familiar question.

'Cups of tea. A few biscuits. I'm not hungry.'

He goes out of the room and returns with a tray. Flaky white plaice, poached in butter; thinly sliced bread and butter. Her father has always done the right thing in a crisis. His compassion gags her: she wants to weep at the sight of the food and dare not.

Sante has waited up for her: she can see the light in the cabin.

'Boys are in bed and asleep signora,' he says. 'I check up. Solicitor come here today: say herd will be sold at auction on Monday: say, sorry to hear about Kurt.'

The bitter, brown face is imploring: she lays a hand on his sleeve,

'Sante, you're a Catholic. Do you believe in prayer?' He nods.

'I tried to pray, Sante: but I can only make bargains.'

'Kurt is very strong man signora: have-a strong mind. Not go under.'

She knows what he means; but doubts that will-power alone can halt death: there is the body's treachery to be reckoned with, and who would have thought it? That strong, fine body: custom made for the lifting of bales and the carrying of corn. Has she not that day seen his chest wired up to a clicking machine? And what price his will-power now?

She discovers new facets in familiar people. Her mother meets trouble with stunned immobility: as if, by remaining unprovocative she will avoid the tragedy that is inherent in living. Cathy feels this same tendency growing within herself: it is her father who sees to it that she eats one meal each day. Invalid food for the fit and healthy.

*

She shops in the Kingsbridge stores for convenience foods: surprised at the new possibilities for feeding a family without actually cooking. Let her sons eat frozen TV dinners and tinned spaghetti: mother has abdicated her role of Hausfrau.

The doctors and nurses tell her nothing. She slips in and out of the side-ward, afraid to ask questions; and then, on the tenth day of his illness the hardware and tubes are removed from Kurt's body, and he is moved into the Medical Ward. Freshly-shaved, and wearing a blue-striped pyjama jacket, she finds him propped up on several pillows and fully conscious.

'Hello,' she says, 'it's been a long time – how are you?' She picks up his hand, pale and thin, how quickly his summer tan has faded. His face is stiff down one side, but no longer grotesque; his body is barely discernible under the smooth white bedspread.

She can feel something split in her chest: oh my love, my love. How can I face you? what have I done or not done to bring you to this sorry state.

The tears spill out of his eyes and run down his face: and she wipes them away with her fingers. 'I need you' he says: 'I have never feel this before: that I need you.'

You need the farm, she thinks. Walk on grass, hear birds sing. Remember my love, Chilton's farm. The beginning.

She says, 'I need you Kurt. We need each other.' At last, they have said it. The moment holds content too tender to bear.

*

She lies awake all that night, body hunched up at the edge of her bed, face turned to the window, waiting for daylight. His body has withstood its crisis, but what of his mind. She begins to take stock of her situation. There is cash in the bank, his hard work and thrift have seen to that. They are due to vacate the farm at the end of September. Six weeks remain during which a house must be purchased, and their possessions transported to Kingsbridge, and how will she manage alone? He has been restored to her: but greatly altered. No worry, no stress, for him in the months to come. Decision is hers. Power at last, to say what they shall or shall not do. The prospect appals her. Her little decisions have only ever been made in the shelter of Kurt's approval.

Almost at once, she has found a house. A shabby Victorian villa that stands in a quiet tree-lined street, on the edge of Kingsbridge. It is too big, too dark, too dilapidated: but it is going cheap, for quick sale, and it has a large garden.

'Cash on the nail,' she tells the house-agent, 'and I must have possession within a month.' Cathy is learning fast. Paul and Martin meanwhile, eat stodge and wear yesterday's shirts. They appear to enjoy it.

*

He is fed from a cup with a spout; like a teapot. Nurses wash him and shave him. An oxygen cylinder stands near his bed: just in case. Nothing moves in his mind. Blank wall: white space. Cathy comes every evening. She holds his hand all the time; the concern in her face makes him cry.

'I need you' he'd said. Gottes wille! what is wrong with you Baumann? Need is for children. But I am a child now. Washed and fed like a baby.

His memory plays tricks; days are shuffled together. 'How long have I been in this place?' he asks Cathy.

'Two weeks.'

'Moorseek?' he asks her: aghast at the sound of his thin, old man's voice.

'Taken care of by Sante; all in order. Don't worry.'

Who is this Sante: and how can he ask her?

'Boring for you, coming here every evening. I can't talk much.'

She smiles. 'Just for once, I don't want you to talk. Just be there.'

'All these years: too busy for talk.' He drifts away into sleep.

They have explained his condition to him in the words he can understand. Small clot of blood in his heart; smaller clot in his head.

Clot! shouts Martin, when Paul annoys him. Clot yourself! Paul replies. Baumann's head and heart. Both clotted.

'Blood like strawberry jam, you must have,' lilts the little Indian nurse. 'It's all that rich food that you Germans eat. You must go on a diet.'

He knows better. The old bomb has gone off inside him: that unexploded missile that had been ticking away for the past twenty years; and who is going to put Humpty-Dumpty together again?

He asks Cathy. 'When I get out of here, can we talk things over?'

'All the time,' she says lightly, 'you know me, chatterbox. Drive you crazy I expect, making up for lost time.'

His stiff face can no longer convey expression. 'No chatter,' he says intently, 'I have to talk about serious matters. Last night I dreamed about Mechtenhausen. Do you know my village?'

'No Kurt, I don't know it.'

'Small village. It stands on a hill, forest all round it. Miles and miles of birchen and tannenbaum. It was a steep climb to get there: but you already know that.'

'I was never in Mechtenhausen, Kurt. That was before the war: before my time.'

'Ach so. You are English aren't you? I had forgotten.'

*

She tells him about the house. 'A garden with trees, and lawn. Large rooms, high ceilings. It needs paint and paper, of course, I'm working on it each day: one room at a time.'

He is fretful. 'I won't like large rooms; and I know nothing of gardens.'

'Well, there is one small room, downstairs. It can be yours, if you like.' She looks tired and thinner. There are lines in her face, and her hair streaked grey.

'Money?' he asks her.

'Plenty left,' she assures him, 'I'll be careful. No mink coats, or weekends in Paris. Not really my style.'

Her style: what is it? He has always taken so much for granted. He can always tell which part of the Kingsbridge house is receiving attention by the shade of the paint which lies thick on her fingernails. Blue means the kitchen.

Think slowly; move slowly. After six weeks in bed he can only achieve the hospital bathroom when supported by nurses on either arm. Grey face, grey hair, stooped shoulders. Gottes Wille, Baumann. Can she still care about you?'

He comes home in the dark, cold month of November; dragging his left leg slightly; unable to wash and dress without her assistance. Kurt Baumann is learning about dependence; he is tired all the time: needs sleep and quiet. He is a wreck of a man.

The strange house settles down around him: its routines are governed by his special needs. His bed has been placed in the little room exactly as she had promised. She sleeps nearby, on a camp bed, in case he needs her. He cannot climb stairs.

*

'There is nothing like a strong hatred to integrate a man's personality. But when that hatred has leaked away, what is left? I have lost my mainspring Cathy. Rage and resentment no longer power me. I am the German whose life has been saved by the English. Good joke eh?

'They showed compassion to me in that hospital. I have been sat with: mourned over, shown concern: and why should they have cared what happened to me?

'Ach ja, Cathy! I was once a good hater. I have hated the Poles who occupy my village; the Russians who raped my womenfolk, and killed my father. I hated those two Canadian sergeants who spat in my face while they stole my watch and the ring my mother gave me. But lately, I have been humbled by kindness. "Coals of fire", in your language. I once had a decoration for bravery Cathy. You didn't know that did you? They pinned it on me in 1944. But the loser's medals have no value Cathy: and that one of mine is better forgotten. A joke really: a little tin cross. The supply of iron had run out when it came to my turn.'

*

Pure woollen sweaters, and fleece-lined slippers, and blazing fires cannot warm him. She does her best.

'How can you be cold?' she cries, 'when the temperature in this room stands at 80°.'

'These drugs,' he explains, 'are to thin my blood and lower my blood-pressure. With water going through my veins at a crawl, how can I keep warm?'

There are other problems. Low-cholesterol diet. None of the rich and spicy foods he has always loved. In no time at all he has lost forty-three pounds in weight.

'I can't get used to this new, skinny husband,' jokes Cathy,

'I can count all your ribs just lately; and it seems odd to see you in a collar and tie, and your second-best suit.'

'So how do you think I feel? Give me *The Times* and a rolled umbrella and I will pass for an Englishman soon.'

These English. I have not hated them; but I have not loved them. Not even you my dearest wife: not as I should have. I have loved your land. Your safe little farmstead, where a man can hide away with his wounded pride and his futile hatreds. Ach ja!

'I have loved the soft blue springtimes of England: the hawthorn, and the dog-rose. I have loved your woods on an autumn evening. The pain flares bright and sharp in my chest when I say this. I do not find confession easy.

'In the hospital there was an elderly sister. The sort you would expect to have a long memory for old enemies: you know what I mean. She only came onto the ward at night. They have a little more time to talk, those nurses who do the night-duty. She was good to me: always knew when the pain was bad, before I could tell her. One night, in case she did not already know it, I said to her, "Do you know that I am German?"

'"Why of course Mr Baumann," she said, "I know it. I was on holiday last year in your country. Nice people, the Germans. Hospitable, friendly. I shall go back there again, next year."

'All these years, have I sometimes imagined hostility, where none existed? Have I found rejection because I sought it? Perhaps we always find what we look for.'

*

She has given thought to the room he lives in. The carpet is brown, and the walls are white: she has hung them with Martin's paintings and bits of bright copper. There is a shelf by his bed which holds books, and the telephone sits at his elbow. His many drugs are set out, in their daily dosage, on a flowered saucer.

The window looks over the garden. There is a dark, paved courtyard bordered by laurel. The granite-filled hump of a rock garden lurks in one corner. A strip of crazy-paving runs off to an untrimmed lawn. Several trees stand knee-deep in the leaves of past autumns. The very thought of the garden tires him.

'For years I denied concentration camps. But you know that Cathy. We Germans are patriots too. I have loved my country because it is my country. When I was a boy I lay down on the dark green moss in the Pommern forest, and heard the heart of Germany beating. Does that label me monster, Cathy?'

'Nobody wins in war,' she says.

'Not true mein schatzchen! Thomas Mann say so. I am reading your books, these days, Cathy. You'll have me a bloody intellectual yet.'

Hatred leaks out, bit by bit, like stuffing from an old mattress: and I am left, a hollow man, with no purpose. Depression, the doctor calls it. He says it will pass; when I weep, she weeps with me. She puts her arms around me: 'We will get over all this,' she says. There are possibilities for hurt that I never dreamed of. I embarrass my sons. Well, I don't blame them. A father who is strong and active is one thing: an invalid is another.

Spring is reluctant this year: green spikes push their way through the frozen earth and Cathy reports each new sighting.

'There are daffodils Kurt. Crocus, I think, under the oak tree. Hundreds of snowdrops in flower along the border. It's a lucky dip; that garden.'

I had acres of wheat and barley, Cathy. I had sugar-beet and potatoes, meadow grass and a river, on Moorseek. You never once spared an interested glance at the view.

There is a fishpond in the rockery: a pink plastic heron stands on one leg, beside it; head bent, looking for non-existent goldfish. She likes the heron. 'Let's keep it,' she says, 'at least, it's better than gnomes.'

How long have I got, I wonder. In war I never once thought about death. Not a scratch Baumann: not a broken fingernail: and look at you now, nursing your old war-wound. Your broken bloody heart. I get maudlin; I pity myself; I am no longer a man.

*

The earth has blossomed; the air has turned mild and she persuades him to leave his room, and take his first walk in the garden. Slowly does it: he is learning to walk, to live again. She wraps a thick woollen scarf around his neck, and guides his stiff left arm to the overcoat sleeve. She averts her eyes as she does so: they never acknowledge that useless arm. His feet are awkward in shoes, after so long. Living hurts and pinches. Easier to die perhaps: but not in a blue, English springtime.

'It's pretty wild at the moment.' She is apologetic. 'The lawns need mowing, as you can see.' Two lawns? Du lieber!

'But it's so exciting Kurt. Things keep popping up out of the ground where you least expect them. I don't know what half of them are, but I have a book.'

Cathy always has the book to refer to. He knows she reads medical journals lately, and manuals on home improvement. Heady stuff after Mann and Goethe.

They are onto the crazy-paving and he is moving strongly. She irons the panic out of her voice. 'Kurt,' she says smoothly, 'shall I fetch your tablets?'

He has halted abruptly in front of the lilac trees and his face is ashen. 'You have not tell me there is Flieder.' He is incoherent. 'There is Flieder Cathy: one white, one blue. They stand together, exactly as they did in my mother's garden.' She becomes alarmed at his frenzy, tries to persuade him away from the spot, but without success.

'Fetch a chair' he orders; and his voice holds the old, sharp note of command. 'I will sit here and observe the Flieder. Ach Gott,' he whispers, 'ist das nicht schön?'

She fetches a chair and sets it beneath the trees. 'Flieder?' she asks. 'Is that what you call it?'

'What is your word?' he demands.

'Lilac' she tells him. 'We call it lilac.'

They have found a new language.

Later on he says, 'There is Schneeglöckchen under the pear tree.' She takes a look: 'Lily-of-the-valley,' she reports back. They move slowly along the path. 'Pansies,' she points out. 'Stiefmütterchen,' he translates. She takes time to work that one out 'Little stepmothers'? What a ridiculous name for a pansy. How did the Germans arrive at that one do you suppose? 'What,' she asks, 'do you say for wallflower?' He doesn't know. She fetches the dictionary from the house, and they name the flowers, in the sunshine.

Turn the clock back, Baumann. Dictionary is in your hand again: and life just beginning.

*

The letters from Germany never bring good news. Over the years she has learned to distrust the Dresden postmark, but this one is stamped 'West Berlin'. Cathy turns the envelope over and reads the name on the flap. 'From somebody called von Riesbach,' she says as she hands it to him. He reads the letter through twice but says nothing, so she takes the single sheet from his hand and begins to read for herself.

'Dear Kurt. We were very sorry to hear of your illness. Christina, as you probably know, writes regularly to us. She has applied for permission to visit you but has been refused. Therefore, as I shall be visiting friends in England, at the end of May, Christina, has asked me to call and see you. If this is acceptable to you, will you please let me know as soon as possible. M. von R.'

Kurt is looking amazed and embarrassed. 'I want no visitors here,' he says firmly, before she can comment. 'I need to be quiet. The doctors say so.'

'But surely this one woman can hardly disturb you. Unless she is some old flame you would rather not meet?'

He grins: 'You couldn't be further away from the truth. Melanie von Riesbach is several years younger than I am, and way above me in the pecking order. If she had even so much as looked my way her father would have horsewhipped us both.'

'My God!' Cathy says, impressed, 'What is she then, some kind of a princess?'

'You might have thought so,' he says bitterly, 'she comes from an old and aristocratic family. The word "von" is the equivalent of Sir or Lady, in your language. The von Riesbachs owned the village of Mechtenhausen before the war. In a way, they owned all of us as well.'

'What do you mean?' Cathy asks, intrigued at this notion of twentieth-century serfdom.

'If you wanted to work – you worked for von Riesbach. If you wanted to eat, have a roof, keep your pigs and chickens, your strip of grazing, your vegetable plot – you bent the knee, and looked cheerful while you did it.' Kurt moves to a chair near the fire, and holds out his cold hands to the blaze. 'I hated von Riesbach. When I was a boy I quarrelled with him: a pretty risky thing to do in that situation. If I remember correctly, I threw some potatoes at him. I thought he would drop down dead from anger: he used his riding crop on me.' Kurt pauses and draws his breath in sharply: 'After that, my parents were forced to send me away from home, to work for another employer. I only came back at week-ends. I never forgave von Riesbach for that.'

'A pretty big noise in the Nazi Party too, I suppose?' asks Cathy. She thinks that she has a clear picture now of this lord-of-the-manor, this Junker. Uniformed, jackbooted, hung about with medals, and old duelling scars. Grinding the people of Mechtenhausen beneath his spurred heel.

Kurt looks astounded. 'Ach no! von Riesbach was never a Nazi. He worked and spoke out against them. You must understand that he was a powerful man in our district. Politically, we were all influenced by him. He was once arrested and held for a time.'

'So he was not altogether a bad man,' Cathy says.

'Well,' Kurt admits, as if the idea is a new one, 'he was certainly anti-Hitler. He was conscripted and sent to the Front though, like everyone else.'

'And after the war?'

'He lost everything. He lives now in a flat in West Berlin. I think he works for the British Control Commission, as an interpreter.'

'But why is your sister so closely involved with these people?'

'Christina was Kindermädchen to the von Riesbach children, there were two of them. Melanie, and a younger child; a boy.' Kurt sounds rueful: 'Myself – I never could understand her attachment to them. Christina really loved that family – especially Melanie. But it looks as though the von Riesbachs have kept in touch with the village people. Christina has mentioned in her letters that they write, and send parcels: give what help they can.'

'That doesn't sound too despotic.'

Kurt holds out a hand, palm upwards, offering her reasons.

'The Frau von Riesbach was a truly good woman. Kind and thoughtful.' He shrugs and pulls down his lips at the corners: 'If I was to meet them now, after twenty years, it might all be different.'

'It seems as if you will have to meet their daughter,' says Cathy, tapping the letter. 'For your sister's peace of mind at least, this Melanie von Riesbach will have to come here.'

Cathy Baumann has her private doubts about this visitor from Berlin, but she suppresses them beneath a welter of housewifely duties. She prepares a bedroom; plans meals several days in advance; and puts out her best pink towels in the bathroom.

She has never met an aristocratic German. She is not quite sure of the form.

*

The London train pulls into Kingsbridge station, and an attractive woman comes down the platform, carrying her own suitcase. There is something about the expensive cut of her short, blonde hair, and the style of her pale blue suit, that shouts 'continental' to Cathy. The guest has arrived.

After the first uneasy skirmishings, it is clear that the lady from West Berlin will be easy to please. She is quietly grateful for the offer of a hot bath after her long journey. She will not expect hotel service, monogrammed silver, haute cuisine. Melanie von Riesbach praises Cathy's roast lamb and mint sauce, and rhubarb crumble. She settles down by the fire like any old Mechtenhausen kamerad from the good old days in Pommern. Kurt is at ease. Cathy can feel his pleased relaxation in her own facial muscles.

Aristocrat or proletarian, it makes no difference: conversations between East Germans always take the same route.

'What happened when the Russians, the Poles –?'

Cathy thinks she has heard it all before, with a few variations. Perhaps Melanie von Riesbach's story will deviate just a little. Hers was no impoverished agricultural family. Having paid the piper, they would have expected to call the tune. Excusing herself from the reminiscing, Cathy leaves the room on a pretext of urgent domestic duties. Kurt does not notice his wife's hasty exit. He is back in the village of Mechtenhausen; has shed thirty years;

is holding a rare and improbable conversation with Melanie von Riesbach, the Junker's daughter.

Cathy straightens an already tidy kitchen, and makes an uncalled for pot of coffee. She pauses beside the sitting-room door, still unwilling to enter; the story is not yet finished.

'My mother and I made a suicide pact,' Melanie is saying, 'she cut my wrists, and then her own. We woke up in a makeshift hospital several hours later. A Russian was sitting beside my bed: a boy who spoke a few words of German. He was very angry with me. He pointed at my bandaged wrists: 'You not believe on God' he scolded, 'if you believe on God you not do this bad thing.' There are livid scars underneath her wide silver bracelets, and Kurt Baumann can see for himself that Melanie, the Junker's daughter, has also suffered.

After four days and nights with the Baumanns, the lady from West Berlin departs, to visit her old friends in London.

'She came here in 1950,' Kurt tells Cathy, 'to train as a nurse in London. Imagine that – a nurse – a von Riesbach! She took SRN pretty good don't you think? To pass her exams, in a foreign language.'

Cathy smiles at his changed direction. 'You seem to have altered your mind about these von Riesbachs.'

He spreads out his hands, palms upwards. 'War,' he explains, 'war changes people.'

*

The summer is easy. He lies in the sun and grows stronger: soon he is able to wash and shave himself, to get dressed without her assistance, and to climb stairs. He takes short walks, alone, in the district; he talks about finding a job. One day he walks too far, too fast, and returns to the house in a state of collapse. Angina Pectoris is the verdict.

Kurt has grown knowledgeable about heart disease in the past few months: 'That's it then,' he tells the doctor, 'nobody ever recovers from that one. How long would you give me?'

'There are drugs Mr Baumann. Life can be prolonged for an indefinite period if you are prepared to be careful. Forget about work; consider yourself prematurely retired.'

'At the age of forty-four?'

'Man, you're a walking miracle anyway. Don't ask for too much. Enjoy what you have: take your time.'

'Angina,' he tells her: and watches her knowing face grow stiff.

'There are tablets,' he says, 'little white ones. I dissolve one under my tongue, and the pain goes away.'

'As long as you're not in pain,' she says.

The winter is harder. Martin gives his father a game of chess when he can. Paul is rarely at home. Cathy is feeling the strain: she is fierce with her sons, and then over-indulgent. If they are confused, so is she. His memory comes back in fragments: jerking like some old reel from a silent movie. They sit in the small brown room every evening: he watches her knitting a sweater for Paul.

'Did I ever tell you what happened in France, when they took us prisoner?'

'Do you think you should talk about that just now? Why not leave it until you are stronger?'

He stirs a blackened log with the toe of his slipper, and watches the apple-wood flare into wild blue flame. 'Now,' he says sharply, 'I have to tell it while it is clear in my mind. I was sent into France in the spring of 1944: pulled out of the Navy in a hurry, and given an army uniform and a rifle. At first it was not too bad; we were in that part called the Riviera. Ach, those big white villas, you should have seen them Cathy. Full of mimosa and cherry blossom, those gardens! For a day or two we sat about in the sunshine: but not for long, quite soon we were on the move. I had served on mine-sweepers, I had been torpedoed, sunk, and rescued, but I had known nothing like France that summer. The heat was suffocating, and I was a sailor, unused to moving on foot. We knew we were losing: there were so few of us left, and our equipment was poor. The British had started to strafe us: we had no time for sleep, only move back and further back every day. During this time I got a letter from my father. From Russia. God knows how it found me, in all that muddle: it was the last letter he ever wrote. "We have lost this war. We are pinned down here: no way out." It had not even been censored. I no longer wrote letters. There seemed no point.'

Kurt pauses, and takes a log from the basket, and thrusts it deep in the dying heart of the fire. 'By the middle of September we were surrounded. Our officers knew it was hopeless, but the order had come from Hitler – no surrender. That final twenty-four hours is clearer than yesterday's sunrise. We were holed up in a damaged bunker. Three of us: a Sergeant Becher, myself, and a boy who should never have left his mother. The boy's name was Hansi: he was an awkward gangling youth, with a thatch of blond hair that dislodged his cap when he moved. Fifteen years old, and straight from the farm to the Wehrmacht. They were sending children up to the front by this time: scared out of their wits by the sights they were bound to witness.'

Kurt looks down at his hands. 'Once I picked up a man's blown-off leg and handed it back to him, like a lady's hanky.'

She says, 'Kurt – I don't think this is a very good idea.'

'We were in this bunker. We hadn't eaten for a couple of days: your planes were really putting the pressure on us. I had never seen anything like it: they came at us in waves, hour after hour. They blacked out the daylight.

'We were half-asleep when this man came staggering into the bunker. I grabbed my rifle, but he shouted "Nicht schiessen!" He was an officer. SS the worst kind. We lay down again and ignored him. I knew it was wrong, but we were exhausted. We couldn't have jumped to salute if he had been Adolf Hitler. "On your feet, you pigs," this officer screamed. "Why are you hiding? I could have you court-martialled for this."

'"Ach, shut up!" says Becher. "The British'll hear you."

' "Get up." the SS man says, very quietly. "Get up, or I will shoot you." I stood up; so did Hansi. Well, discipline has to be maintained at all times, or civilisation breaks down. The boy was so weak he kept falling over. The officer stood over Becher, but a rustling sound made him lose concentration for just a few seconds, and the sergeant shot him from a sitting position. He scored a bull's eye, straight through the officer's forehead. The rat that had made the noise sat quite still. I couldn't believe it had happened. "We shall be court-martialled for this," I shouted. "Don't be a bloody fool Baumann," Becher said, "you're not in the Navy now." I dragged the SS man into a corner and covered him with his own coat. The rat sat beside him. Waiting.'

'Stop it,' says Cathy. 'I don't want to hear this.'

'We executed that officer,' says Kurt, 'He was my age. He might have been married; with children.'

'But you said he was SS. The worst kind.'

'Every university graduate was conscripted to the SS. They had no more choice in the matter than we did. He might have been one of the good ones.' He pauses, 'It unhinged that boy's mind, you know. When the next wave of bombers flew over, he ran out to meet them. Ran through that field like a crazy rabbit, and was blasted to bits. I wanted to leave the bunker after the boy was killed, but Becher said no. Well, I was the corporal and he was the sergeant. After a time it went very quiet. We crawled to the door and looked out, and there they were, all around us. Your tanks. Your bloody great tanks, with their guns trained on us.'

'You were alive and unhurt: you can be grateful for that much.'

'I was not grateful: I was angry; to have gone through all that for nothing. They lined us up, and two Canadian sergeants collected our rings and our watches. They tipped out our wallets and trampled our photographs into the mud. They laughed, and spat in our faces. Hatred breeds hatred, Cathy.' He sighs: 'They brought us to England, six weeks later. By this time we had dysentery, lice, high fever. We stank: were like animals. In the prison camp they gave us hot baths and haircuts, and clean clothing. We were fed, and allowed to sleep; but hundreds of older men died. Men like my father.'

'You have never talked about any of this before,' she says.

'When I was strong,' he says, 'I had no time for thinking.'

Another spring, another summer: and the doctors have got the dosage wrong. Or perhaps it is the chemistry of his body that has changed. Too much of one drug in your system, they tell him, and not enough of another. No problem. Your blood is too thin Mr Baumann, you are haemorrhaging from your kidneys. A few weeks in the hospital, and we'll have you as good as new!

'There is a Polish man in the bed on my right-hand side,' he tells her. Cathy sits by the bed and clutches his hand as if it is she who is drowning. 'A very sick Polish man: he has arthritis, and a wonky ticker. He is waiting to have a gall-bladder operation; and I thought that I had problems! This man was an officer in the Polish army: he fought with the British. He's a hell of a bloke, you know Cathy. He's the sickest man in the ward, but he's got guts. I find myself respecting him, can you credit that? This Polish man is my friend! The last of my hatred is flooding down the hospital drain, with the blood from my rotten kidneys. All gone. All clear now.'

*

Life arranges itself in a different pattern. Once again the years are quiet: apple-flavoured. His doctor's skill, and the re-emergence of Kurt Baumann's old truculent spirit, are to ensure him another nine years of life. The farm-bred boys turn out to be artistic, and go away to study their subject. Their absence is a reprieve; their presence had become an obligation she is no longer able to fulfil. It is time for her pattern to come full circle: once, long ago, it had been a repetition of valleys, now she returns to the concentrated living of life in a single room.

The hot little room holds all the clutter of their changed lives. The stereo and TV: her books, his chess-board. She grows flowers in pots on the window-sill, and he burns apple-logs in the fire grate. Proximity breeds dependence; and dependence deepens into need. She leaves the house for short intervals: to change library books and do shopping. He is always waiting, door half-open, for her return. The pottery class is held on a Thursday night in the school around the corner. 'No,' he says, 'I don't want you to go.'

'It will only be for a couple of hours.'

'There will be plenty of time for that sort of thing in the years to come. But not now; not just now.'

Pain does not go away by itself: and once again he must learn his own limits. Angina pectoris becomes his master. It obliges him to walk slowly, squeezes his chest, commands respect and obedience. It is parent, teacher, Wehrmacht. One of these fine days it will destroy him.

*

He has that secretive, withdrawn look that means pain. He will conceal it from her when he can. That evening he goes into the kitchen. She can hear him clattering cups and cutlery, setting the tray and the breakfast table. These are his regular, self-appointed duties. His sheet anchor.

When the silence has lasted a full three minutes she calls his name. But he does not answer.

It is to be the City Hospital this time. He is wheeled through a Casualty Ward full of drunks and addicts. It is New Year's Day, and the population has been out celebrating. The thugs and the hooligans, and the innocent bystanders are waiting in line for running repairs. The stretcher is wheeled at speed: heart-failure rates priority. Cathy sits on a metal chair, while the addicts moan, and the vomiting drunks fall around her. After thirty minutes by the clock on the wall, she is led to Intensive Care.

The hardware is banked up all around him. The drips and the meters, the oxygen cylinder; the TV monitor and the cardiograph machine. The tanks, the bloody great English tanks, have their guns trained on him. She sees that someone has already removed the watch from his wrist and the ring from his finger. She knows that this time he has no fight left in him: no anger. His pattern has come full circle. They exchange one long look but no words.

It takes him an hour to die. The Sister invites her to watch, 'most people prefer to,' she says, as if this is some Saturday afternoon spectator sport, and Cathy is in danger of missing something. Although she is standing outside, in the corridor, she knows the exact moment that he stops breathing.

There must be some recognised mode of behaviour, but she doesn't know what it is. Her state of mind has always depended from day to day upon Kurt's approval: and so she reacts as she thinks he would have her do. By this time her family are with her. Martin alone is weeping. Nobody touches her shoulder: nobody comforts her. Nobody claims her.

*

In other years the hyacinths have bloomed too early or too late. This time she has achieved the miracle: they came into flower on Christmas Day, and are still blooming. She can smell the flowers as soon as she enters the house: she is quite alone, on her own insistence. In the hot little room, the perfume is overpowering. She touches a switch, and every separate waxy floret assaults her eye. The pink and the blue, and the white ones: fresh and alive in the lamplight. The hyacinths stand in wide white bowls on the window-sill. Before she takes off her coat, she unlocks the door that leads into the garden. She carries each bowl of flowers outside, and sets it down on the frost-rimed earth. She re-enters the house and hangs her coat in the wardrobe. The flowers will be dead by morning.

She begins to tidy the room. Pillows and cushions are scattered about on the carpet: a glass of water, jogged by a doctor's elbow has left a damp patch in an armchair. She mops and tidies and straightens. She fetches a cardboard box, a large one, and in it she places the items her husband had touched on the previous evening. His spectacles lie on an open book; the remains of his supper tray stand on the coffee-table. When she has removed all signs of his occupation from the room, she picks up the box and carries it into the bedroom. In the end, several boxes are needed to hold all her husband's possessions: she works methodically through the night, emptying drawers and cupboards. When she has finished, she ties up the cartons with string, and lines them up in the hall, for collection.

*

Only a week ago she had bought a new winter coat: strawberry-coloured wool, expensive. She fetches the coat and lays it out flat on the carpet. She takes up the scissors and cuts the fine worsted, first into strips, and then into tiny squares. She stirs the logs into flame and carefully burns every inch of her new, bright coat.

In the kitchen she finds the breakfast tray that he has laid ready for morning. Two cups and saucers, two plates, two knives and forks. She moans aloud: just once. She picks up the loaded tray and carries it out to the dustbin.

She persuades her parents to stay at home. It is January; her father is ill; and her mother is temperamentally unsuited to funerals. If it was possible, she would hold the burial service under the lilac trees in the garden, with herself as sole and chief mourner.

When they lower the coffin into the earth she averts her eyes. A burly, heavily-bearded man named Paul stands beside her; a tall thin boy called Martin is openly weeping. She sheds no tears. She wonders vaguely where all these people have come from.

She returns to her house at once, and alone. On her own insistence. The mopping and cleaning, the packing of cartons, has all been for nothing. He has left his imprint upon the air: is more vibrant in death, if that is possible, than he has been in life. It is as if he sits in his chair by the fire and mourns his own passing, with her. How many times has he told her, that she cannot live without him? If she concentrates hard enough, she can see his foot, in its checked-felt slipper, at rest on the hearthrug. Or his hand, the left one that bears the wedding ring, at ease, on the arm of the chair. She can never call up his face, no matter how hard she tries.

The curtains stay closed long after the funeral. She cannot bear even the winter sunshine. If she must mourn, let the world mourn with her. Her family begin to fear for her sanity. She has, they suspect, been a little unhinged, by former events of much slighter trauma.

A whole year passes: letters come from Berlin and Dresden. Melanie von Riesbach is offering her sanctuary, but like everything else, the invitation to visit Berlin remains unanswered. People, who should know about such things, assure her that grief lasts six months, a year, no longer. Longer than that is not normal. One year of weeping is permitted; after that, the world loses patience.

*

In the early spring of the second year of her widowhood, she picks up the receiver and dials the magic number. The voice at the end of the line says 'Samaritans – can I help you?' She holds the receiver close to her ear and waits.

The man has a soothing voice. 'Don't worry if you are finding it hard to begin,' he says, 'it happens to lots of people. My name is Harry, and I will be here for as long as you want me.'

Not so, Harry! Nobody ever stays for as long as you want them.

'Are you still there? Can you try to tell me your trouble? I will help if I can: just take it slowly.'

She şays, in an icy voice, 'I am very sorry. I've wasted your time. I know what I need to do after all.'

The voice of the man called Harry is suddenly urgent. 'Can you say where you're phoning from? Just for the record you know.'

He is still pleading for information when she lays the receiver down.

*

Her family agree too readily that a holiday in Berlin is the only answer. They do not visualise Kurt, as she does, standing beside the Brandenburg Gate, miraculously resurrected, still wearing the uniform of the Kriegsmarine, as he does in the photograph on the table. Perhaps after all, she will find him there, suitcase and bunch of lilac in hand, en route for his beloved Mama, and Mechtenhausen.

The travel agent finds her amusing. The heat of his office, and the demented frieze of coloured brochures have triggered her migraine. She puts on her tinted glasses.

'A ticket to West Berlin?' the young man chortles, 'Well, you won't need your sunglasses there in March, will you madam?'

Part Seven

1979

They had been travelling for some time through open country, and in brilliant sunshine. She could see mile after mile of rich brown earth undergoing intense cultivation. Great stands of beech and fir stretched towards and beyond the horizon; the land rolled up to the train like an uninterrupted sea; for, as Kurt had so often told her, there were no hedges. Suddenly Jürgen Hecht pointed out a separate band of ploughed earth. 'That strip runs for hundreds of miles,' he told her, 'it's packed full of land-mines. It's an open wound that is never going to be allowed to heal over.'

Almost at once they came up to the border, and she saw for herself what the East Germans meant by an Iron Curtain. This was no double strand of barbed-wire strung out across frontier posts. These were fortifications: incredibly complicated, cunningly designed, and manned with an efficiency that must make escape a lethal proposition for anyone who was desperate enough to attempt it. The railway station at Marienborn was eerily silent. Only armed guards and Transportspolizei were allowed to approach the Berlin train. They were urging their unmuzzled Alsatians to sniff and search underneath each carriage: 'God help anybody,' commented Jürgen, 'who attempts to escape from the DDR by this route.'

Passengers were beginning to leave their seats and peer curiously out of the corridor windows. Cathy could hear the shock in the voices of Dutch and Italian travellers. It was one thing to read about this German frontier in the papers – quite another, to see it. The 'Trapos', working in gangs of three, and using a short metal ladder, proceeded to search the train from end to end, and from top to bottom. She could hear the crashing of doors as the toilets and luggage compartments were entered.

'It's just like a third-rate spy film,' she said to Jürgen.

'Make no mistake,' he assured her, 'these boys are not acting.'

The compartment door slid back, and a man in a smart green uniform blocked the sunlight. He obviously carried more authority than the blue-clad 'Trapos'. A broad leather strap around his neck supported a metal tray filled with rubber stamps and inkpads. There was a total silence while he examined their passports.

Satisfied, he applied a series of rubber stamps, and returned their papers to them but did not at once depart. He made a prolonged and unembarrassed study of both their faces, and then, without comment he slid the door to. Although the sunlight had been restored, Cathy shivered.

*

The train had been halted for over an hour and still showed no sign of departing. Cathy stood by the corridor window and looked out on the peeling façade of Marienborn station. Gigantic posters had been positioned at regular points up and down the platforms: they depicted a tightly clenched fist, with the index finger pointing inscrutably heavenwards. The slogan, in yard high letters explained: 'Thirty Years Anniversary of the DDR 1949–1979.'

Jürgen Hecht stood beside her. 'You still haven't told me why you are going to Berlin.'

She moved her shoulders unhappily, 'My sister-in-law is anxious to see me, and Melanie has said I can stay in her flat for as long as I want to –'

'But surely,' he interrupted, 'a visit to your sister-in-law will involve you in crossing the Wall?'

'I know,' she said gloomily, 'it's not an inviting prospect. We haven't met for twenty-five years; my German's not fluent either.'

'Why go then?'

'Can't you see, Mr Hecht? I have to. Christina will want to know about Kurt's last hours. There are certain things that only I can tell her. She was never allowed to visit England, in spite of his illness.'

'My God,' he said sourly, 'you are almost exaggeratedly German in your attitudes. Duty, obligation, and so forth. How did that happen?'

'It's contagious,' she said, 'like measles.'

'You're not looking forward to this meeting are you?'

'Not much.'

'I think,' said Jürgen reflectively, 'that your husband would have left his family in '48, with you or without you. What normal young man spends his life considering his mother? You are also a widow Mrs Baumann: have your sons gathered round to support you?'

'No,' she said thoughtfully, 'you're quite right – they haven't. But my situation is different. I am not a refugee; my financial position is secure; and in any case I believe that the young should be free and unhampered.'

'Perhaps your mother-in-law and Christina took the same view.'

'I don't know,' she said heavily, 'I seem to have based so many of my conclusions on assumptions.'

After an hour and a half of hectic activity within and without, the Berlin train was declared to be innocent of defectors, and allowed to proceed on its way. The man in green travelled with them. In the company of the 'Trapos' he patrolled the corridors at irregular intervals, peering in at the seated passengers, occasionally re-checking their passports and matching up faces with photographs.

*

Cathy leaned back in her seat and drank the hot coffee that Jürgen had ordered. The redundant RESERVIERT signs were still slotted above their heads, even though the remaining four seats remained empty. The train was not crowded. She could have transferred to another compartment at any time in the past ten hours: so why had she not done so? She surely resented this man who probed and dissected as if she was some pinned insect?

Over the rim of the thick railway china she observed Jürgen Hecht, and knew him to be a disturbing man. His hooded brown eyes seemed to look straight into her mind. She could actually feel the log-jam in her emotions shifting and loosening.

Conscious of her close scrutiny of him, Jürgen Hecht looked uneasy. 'Yes,' he said, as if she had asked him a question, 'to have a foot in both camps is an invidious position for any thinking person.' His voice became rough-edged: 'The Germans have always been misunderstood by the English.'

Cathy smiled. 'You have such a chip on your shoulder – and yet you really expect me to ease the weight with half a dozen words?'

'You prevaricate,' he said angrily, 'can you never give a straight answer?'

'All right,' she said decisively, sitting up-right in her corner: 'I'll tell you what I believe, but it won't be what you want to hear. You won't like it.'

Cathy rubbed her right temple. 'You see Mr Hecht: it's quite simple. The answer is that it doesn't matter.' She looked down at her knotted fingers. 'Once, I had something precious. I had this sweet, very special man whom I loved. I stood by and watched him torturing himself with a million doubts: and I never once tried to help him. I could have said – forget it! All the hatred and guilt, and the apportioning of blame, it's all academic now: a game for historians to play at. All that has ever really mattered is you and me, and what we have achieved between us.' She paused, 'Well, I never said it: and now it's too late.' She hesitated: 'I'm not a religious woman Mr Hecht, but I think that man Christ had it all sorted out pretty clearly. He had a single word for what matters most in the human condition. He called it "love".'

Jürgen Hecht was silent for several minutes. At last he said reluctantly, 'You are right, I suppose, in some respects: and it works very well between individuals. After all, you and I have proved it. You loved Kurt; I love Helen. But are you seriously suggesting that those East German guards back on Marienborn station are "lovable" people?'

'I haven't worked out that aspect of it,' Cathy admitted, 'but you have to make a start somewhere don't you? I know that I sound naive: but one step at a time, and slowly is the answer. I have tried so hard all these years to see both points of view at once, that I've ended up with a sort of mental vertigo. But I believe we should always stop short of active hatred. Put love in its place Mr Hecht, and then see what happens.'

*

Jürgen looked exhausted, and frailer than ever. The events at Marienborn station had plainly upset him. He closed his eyes momentarily; and then said abruptly, 'You mentioned just now that you are financially secure –' He grinned at the sight of her raised eyebrows, 'I know, I know,' he said swiftly, 'it's not done is it, in England to enquire about another person's financial status? But I do have a genuine reason for asking.'

'Are you ill Mr Hecht?'

'It shows that badly does it?'

'I'm afraid so. What is it?'

'Cancer. They give me six months.' He spoke without any emotion: 'I want to make everything simple for Helen: ease her into widowhood gently – if such a thing is possible.'

'Oh, it's possible,' Cathy assured him. Her voice shook slightly: 'I receive a pension from the West German government; I will write down the details for you, if you like: where to apply and so on.'

'I would be grateful,' he said, in the tone of a man who is winding up an involved business venture. 'I do not like to leave loose strings unfastened.' He smiled wryly. 'I was unwilling to make this journey alone. Before I left home last night Helen said that I would be sure to find someone congenial to talk to. She could never have guessed that you, Mrs Baumann, would turn out to be such a gift.'

'A gift?'

'You have given me most of the answers I looked for.'

Cathy said quietly, 'I suppose I should sympathise with you. Most people would.'

'But you cannot?'

'Not really; you see, I would be thankful to know how much longer I must be forced to go on coping with living.'

'But you don't intend to, do you? Go on coping, I mean.'

She was silent.

'In the old days,' said Jürgen, 'the Indian widows practised "suttee". They threw themselves onto their husband's funeral pyre. A revolting custom.'

'I coped well enough when Kurt needed me,' she reminded him sharply.

'Then why can't you survive for your own sake?'

'Perhaps I don't want to,' she said. 'Oh, I keep a stiff upper lip. After all, I am British. We are bred to take life on the chin. But I rarely protest, I just nip and tuck: I wheel and veer, and then I back off. Kurt called it cheating.'

*

They were travelling slowly now, through deep forest. Jürgen's pale face was in shadow. 'You are leaving it rather late aren't you?' he asked softly. 'This train hasn't crashed after all, and solved all your problems for you.' He smiled into his cup of coffee: 'Of course, you could act like an East German defector when we reach the next station. The "Trapos" will make a clean job of it, for you. They're fast on the trigger.'

'And cause an international incident?'

'No problem for you Mrs Baumann: you're finished with living.'

Jürgen Hecht was enjoying himself: he warmed to his subject. 'But perhaps you have planned to stage your demise in Berlin. Death in a foreign city can be made to look accidental can't it? and who would suspect a respectable lady like you of wanting to end her own life.'

'You're sending me up Mr Hecht,' she said stiffly.

'Not at all, my dear lady.' His tone was abrasive. 'If you really want to die I will help you. Now how can I be of service?'

'When I need your help – if I need your help,' she said dryly, 'I'll ask you.'

*

The sun was setting as they reached Potsdam. She looked out at the darkening lake and the ancient buildings and felt an unusual desire to say something that would sound both relevant and symbolic. 'Perhaps,' she said diffidently, 'we could make a small treaty of our own. I will try to hold on a bit longer – if you will.'

He laughed abruptly. 'Well you're full of surprises aren't you?

But haven't you noticed? The promises made in Potsdam turn out pretty badly. You saw the man-traps and watchtowers back there.'

It was quite dark now. Place names flashed up at them out of the darkness – Nicolasee, Wannsee, Steglitz.

Jürgen Hecht stood up and began to gather his luggage together: all that paraphernalia that had annoyed her so much in the early morning in Holland. He extended his hand and she took his dry, brittle fingers.

'I shall not forget you, Mrs Baumann.'

'Nor I you, Mr Hecht.'

'Don't do anything foolish, will you.'

They were running into the blessed and beautiful lights of freedom; Zoobahnhof, West Berlin. Cathy looked at her wrist-watch. Eleven hours and forty-five minutes had passed since the continental express had pulled out of the Hook van Holland.

Part Eight

Berlin 1979

Her sense of disorientation was so great on waking that she lay for several seconds, bemused by the swags of yellow flowers that were rioting wildly across the wallpaper of her bedroom. She was in West Berlin: in Melanie von Riesbach's flat. Beyond the draped nets and gold velvet curtains a strange city hummed and threatened.

Cathy's memory of the previous evening was blurred by weariness. She remembered Kürfurstendamm: the blaze of coloured neon, the winking of scarlet rear lights, the slight bumping motion as they had driven at speed over cobbled highways.

'Have you had a good journey?' Melanie had asked her. Cathy, dazzled by streaming lights had answered vaguely, 'I met a middle-aged German man on the train: an ex-patriate Berliner. We had a peculiar conversation.' At the memory of Jürgen Hecht she came fully awake: and suddenly she had an overwhelming desire to be back in Kingsbridge. She missed her pink-shaded bedside lamp, and the little gilt clock that Kurt had once given her.

*

She found that she was alone in the flat: and in fact, a confused recollection came back to her now, of Melanie saying something about an early morning start, since her job as a social worker involved a long drive to the other side of the city. A continental-style breakfast had been set out in the blue and white kitchen; fresh rolls and butter, a selection of home-made preserves, and an egg to boil, if she felt so inclined.

The sun was coming in through a long, uncurtained window, and she rushed to find her dark glasses. Already, she could detect the signs of incipient headache; there was something about this kitchen that brought back a poignant memory of Dietkirchendorf and Kurt's Tante Emma. It could only be, she decided, the pervasive smell of herbs and spices found in all German kitchens, that made it seem so familiar to her.

She wandered about the flat on that first morning, lingering in doorways, absorbing the atmosphere of an unknown woman's home. Closely-packed books on white painted shelves reached from floor to ceiling; and on the walls there were several seascapes in heavy gilt frames, all signed M. von R. All the rooms were furnished with priceless antiques; the parquet was strewn with pale, oriental rugs, and there were several small tables decked out with little laced-edged cloths. There were even anti-macassars on the blue velvet armchairs, and a potted palm standing in one corner. The double white doors in the drawing-room led out to a small stone balcony that overhung Mechner Strasse. As far as Cathy could see, in every direction, the streets of the city were planted with linden trees.

It was April in West Berlin, and she found herself looking down on a vista of pale green treetops. She could not understand why the sight of the lindens should move her; after all, she had never been much of a nature lover. But her tears switched on these days like a well-oiled run-in engine. She experienced no lump in the throat, no pricking eyelids. Her weeping was effortless and without a single hitch. It was, she thought, a doubtful kind of achievement.

*

'I am afraid I shall have to leave you alone here for part of the day,' Melanie had told her, 'but I will try to get back a bit earlier while you are here. I would like to show you Berlin.' The last few words had been said with self-conscious pride: but Cathy was not too sure that she wanted to see Berlin. The very word held unpleasant overtones: it called up images from old, movietone newsreels: the Reichstag burning; tanks rumbling over cobblestones; snipers in dark doorways. She had been given a set of house-keys on her arrival, but she was reluctant to venture out by herself. There were certain sights and sounds that must be avoided; her distress at the sound of spoken German was, she knew, unreasonable and neurotic. She longed to locate the Stettinerbahnhof, but thought that even if such a place still existed she would never dare to approach it. Suppose she should see a flower-seller at the station entrance, selling blue and white lilac? She would be quite certain then that her mind was completely unhinged.

Every day she sat out on the balcony, in the pale spring sunshine: suspended above herself and the city of West Berlin. She watched the people going up and down Mechner Strasse: children with satchels, women with shopping bags, men carrying briefcases, elderly couples walking the dachshund or English terrier. It all looked so normal: so peaceful. As if the horror of Marienborn station, and the man on the train who was dying of cancer, had occurred in some late-night television extravaganza: the sort of drama that most people find it hard to believe in.

The Junker's daughter was turning out to be kind and thoughtful (as had been her mother). She showed Cathy her city as promised; all those green and astonishingly beautiful places, that no one expects to find in a beleaguered outpost. They drove out to the Grünewald lakeside, took the ferry across to the Peacock Island, strolled by the Wannsee, and explored in the Tiergarten.

The days passed slowly: two weeks, three weeks, and she finally found the courage to walk alone in the streets. She discovered her own park bench, her own small café, a favourite early-morning walk by the river. Here in Berlin she lacked the sustaining props and stays of her grief. There were none of those agonised daily visits to lay fresh flowers on Kurt's grave. No bi-weekly trips to the public library, made slowly, to eke out time. No scrappy meals on a tray, consumed absentmindedly while watching television. Her grief was beginning to take on a different aspect: it had a less bitter, more bearable flavour. It was not abating: if anything it became more acute. But the urge to destroy her own life was no longer present. In retrospect she could hardly recall having planned such final and positive action.

She had not wanted to love this city, would never have believed that it was possible for her to do so, and yet the enchantment had gripped her. Here in Berlin her deepest scars had begun to heal over: and she could not deny it.

*

Crossing the Berlin Wall was not to be the straightforward business of being checked in through a single barrier that she had expected. She found herself standing in line with a score of other people, moving slowly from one point of scrutiny to another.

This particular crossing was housed in the busy railway station at Friedrichstrasse; she could hear the passing trains as they rumbled and roared overhead. By the time she had reached the booth where her passport was taken away for a closer examination, she felt cold and frightened. There were stories told in the English newspapers, about people who vanished while crossing this border. Could it be that the German name on her British Passport was causing the guards to view her with increased suspicion?

Of course, nothing happened: why should it? Her handbag was thoroughly searched, her compact opened, her lipstick unswivelled, her papers gone over a dozen times. But hadn't Melanie already warned her that this might happen?

Her passport was returned at last by a grim-faced official, and she was casually nodded in through the final turnstile.

A woman stood at the barrier railings: a handsome, high-coloured woman whose eyes were anxious. Cathy thought that she had prepared herself for this meeting: she had rehearsed the German words she would need when describing Kurt's last illness; had even tried to inject some steel in her wavering backbone. But it made no difference. Christina Leuchner's physical likeness to her dead brother was truly shocking. Cathy knew that she would have picked out this single woman from thousands. There was the same silver hair, the same high cheekbones and deepest eyes, the firm jawline. They came together awkwardly, shaking hands and muttering incoherent greetings, exactly as they had done all those years ago in Dietkirchendorf. They walked away from the station in an uneasy silence, out into the drabness of East Berlin.

Cathy found herself trembling slightly. She had travelled so far to achieve this meeting: but now, face to face with Christina, she was no longer sure of her purpose in coming.

*

The Asiatic Museum in East Berlin is housed in a series of monolithic buildings, linked together by small paved courtyards. They came up to an isolated bench that stood underneath the boughs of an almond tree; Christina halted, and motioned that they should sit down. A chill little wind was tossing the heads of the daffodils in their concrete tubs, and quickening the steps of the Russian and Chinese tourists as they hurried towards the warmth of the museum's Gasthof. Christina Leuchner had clearly chosen a spot where her sister-in-law's halting, heavily-accented German would not draw inquiring glances.

Cathy shivered inside her sheepskin jacket. East Berlin was different. She could smell the fumes of high octane petrol given off by the passing traffic: a distinctive unpleasant odour that is rarely encountered in western countries. She had seen no bustling throngs on the pavements of this strange city, no shop windows packed full of luxury items, no smiling people. But she had seen that impressive avenue called Unter den Linden, and its abrupt termination at the Brandenburg Gate. So far – and no further. That was the order in East Berlin, and how well it applied in her case. She knew now that this was to be the last corner she would ever back into. All her wheeling and veering, her nipping and tucking would have to be ended right here in this museum courtyard.

She began to think about Willi Meyer: that ruined young airman who had so feared rejection by his own kind. She recalled the way she herself had shouted, all those years ago, at that astonished British colonel in Hanover. 'Beyond the pale' was how she described her position in those days! 'His people won't help us either,' she had cried, 'we seem to have broken some unwritten law.'

She stared at the nodding daffodil heads, and her vision blurred as she looked at the past. Was this, after all, the truth of the matter? Was hatred stronger than love when the chips were really down?

And what price courage?

She remembered Inge Zeigenfeltz. So young, so bitter, and yet still snapping back at life. She had not gone under. Inge had straightened the seams of her stockings, applied a fresh coat of lipstick – and set out for England.

And Melanie von Riesbach? Sensitive, cultured, aristocratic; but damaged irreparably in some region of the spirit at which Cathy could only guess. Melanie had also suffered deeply in the war, but now it was she who was offering love and sanctuary to Kurt Baumann's English widow.

A hand on her arm brought her back to the present. Christina was turning to face her. She was holding out both her hands with that un-English gesture that had always embarrassed Cathy. 'Liebe Cathy,' she said gently, 'Liebe Schwester.'

No one had ever called her sister; no one, since Kurt, had spoken to her with affection, or claimed her: and this time it was the totally unexpected that disarmed her; she could feel her eyelids pricking, and the lump was back in her throat.

Part Nine

The boat train left Parkestone Quay, Harwich, at twenty past seven in the morning. Cathy watched the little East Anglian towns growing sharp and clear in the warm May sunshine. Stowmarket, Cambridge, Bury St Edmunds. She let the soft English names ripple gently across her mind. England, she thought, had its own special flavours and textures: its own blend of stoical humour. It was only a woman like her, with myopic vision, and eye turned permanently inwards, that would need to distance herself all those hundreds of miles, in order to see her own birthplace clearly.

The boat train was headed north, bound for Sheffield. By noon she would find herself back in Kingsbridge once again: fitting a key in the lock of her own front door.

The transition would not be easy. She would have to take up all those painful burdens: the memories and the regrets, the conviction of failure. Her experiences in Berlin would be soon forgotten, and she would inevitably assume all her old despairing attitudes towards life and the problems of living.

Briefly, she thought of Jürgen Hecht. 'But, you're finished with living,' he had said, with contempt.

Did she want that to be her epitaph? Peacefully: in Berlin, was the way she had meant it to end. Well, it hadn't happened: and now she was faced with a reckoning.

*

The unmistakable smells of an English breakfast were filling the corridors and compartments. The mingled odours of toast and coffee, and eggs and bacon, reminded her that several hours had elapsed since her last meal. Incredibly, she was hungry.

In the dining car she ordered the lot: sausage and bacon, egg and tomato, fried bread and mushrooms, topped off with a pile of buttered toast, and the kind of chunky marmalade never discovered beyond the shores of England.

When she finally raised her eyes from her plate she saw that the two young men in the opposite seat were regarding her with unconcealed amusement.

'You certainly needed that,' said one.

She smiled as she poured out a cup of coffee. 'I believe I did,' she admitted, 'I hadn't eaten since leaving Berlin.'

'Here,' said the boy, producing a dark-green bottle, 'have a tot of rum in your coffee.

Cathy raised her eyebrows. 'At this time of the morning?'

'We're merchant seamen,' he explained, 'just off ship, going home after two years absence.'

To her amazement she heard herself saying 'All right – I'll drink to that with you,' and she smiled again as she watched his tattooed hand pour a generous measure of rum in her steaming coffee. The smell of the spirit made her feel sick, but she drank it all down.

The small human contact had lightened her mood, and warmed by the rum, she raised up her cup in a toasting gesture.

'Here's to a good homecoming,' she said, 'for you and for me.'

*

Alone again in her window seat, she watched the flat green fields of the Midlands slip by her: and with the sight came a pang of her old depression. Grimly, she fought against it, determined to find the truth of the matter. Could it be, she thought, just possible, that by deferring to the needs and wishes of those she had loved, she had somehow denied her own self? There was, she recalled, a secret place in her house; a bureau drawer that she never opened. It held those little green notebooks, the journals she had kept all those years ago in Dietkirchendorf.

Perhaps she would try to write it all down: discover the truth of her life and Kurt's; a testament she could hand on to her sons. The material lay close to her hand: and the story was not yet ended.

LEO DAYS

PATRICIA WENDORF

Ruth Flemming is a wealthy volunteer worker in the turbulent inner-city district of St Joseph's. By day she gives support to battered wives, lonely old ladies and one-parent families. By night she returns to her elegant home in the upper-class Hillcrest area, secure behind the long driveway and wrought-iron gates.

But one day her well-ordered life is disrupted from within when she discovers her husband, Harry, has left her. Suddenly she is at one with her clients, whose men leave them regularly; for other women, other cities, other lives. But Ruth is a survivor. In the heart of St Joseph's she finds room to vent her frustrations, face her fears, and finally accept love when it is offered to her.

'It is meant to be difficult to write second novels but this is, again, outstanding.' Andrew Marr, *Scotsman*

'*Leo Days* can only consolidate the author's reputation. It is a delicate and skilfully observed account of what life has to offer – and take away – and is above all a delightful novel.'
Elizabeth Bunster, *Books & Bookmen*

'An immensely satisfying book, short, sharp, and very much to the point.' Noeleen Dowling, *Image*

FUTURA PUBLICATIONS
FICTION
0 7088 3448 5

LEFT OF NORTH

JAMES FRIEL

This story begins in the North. It begins on the day that Denise Monton and her best friend, Deborah Ridley, had a fight up on the Rucks – and the Rucks opened up and swallowed Deborah whole. It ends – if end it does – somewhere to the left of North.

For though it was Deborah who died and Denise who lived, Deborah's ghost would not be put to rest. Soon Denise believed that she had killed Deborah; and not long after the rest of the town believed it as well. Ostracized and harassed, the Montons fled the slag heaps of Little Atherton for the tower blocks of Angel, Islington. And there things, as they will, went from pretty bad to truly awful. As Denise's mother said, philosophically, 'We're fated, cruelly fated. We're like the Kennedys or the Barlows off *Coronation Street*. Tragedy stalks us.' Except, of course, that neither the Kennedys nor the Barlows had Deborah Ridley's ghost stalking them as well.

LEFT OF NORTH

James Friel's brilliant brew of black humour and sharp-edged satire.

'His sense of dialogue and detail verges on the wicked . . . uniting kitchen sinker and satire, it's a mischievously compulsive read' – *Time Out*

FUTURA PUBLICATIONS
FICTION
0 7088 3667 4

Futura

ANGEL CAKE

HELEN HARRIS

'My old lady turned out to be an absolute fright. Serves me right, I suppose. She wears bold theatrical make-up on a shrivelled face; bright scarlet lipstick which bleeds into the deep folds of her crinkled lips and orangey pink powder which wobbles on the hairs of her chin . . . She wouldn't let me in at first.'

Alicia Queripel, a retired actress, lives alone with her memories in Shepherd's Bush. Until the day Alison Woodgate appears on her doorstep to visit the old lady she has been 'allocated' by Age Concern. Alicia, suspicious, is at first reluctant to be patronized by a mousy do-gooder. They seem to enjoy little in common. How could Alison's boy-friend Rob compare with Alicia's dear departed Leonard, a paragon among men?

As the weeks pass, however, an unlikely friendship develops over tea and cakes and slowly, through the mingled layers of memory and imagination, an unsuspected pattern starts to emerge.

'the old woman is a totally convincing, rather surprising character and Alison is immensely likeable . . . *Angel Cake* is well worth reading' Susan Hill, *Good Housekeeping*

'a fascinating evocation of what life was like in the English theatre in the 1930s cleverly interwoven with the hopes and fears of a young woman of today' *Yorkshire Post*

'a story of immense beauty and sadness, written with a rare compassion' *Jewish Chronicle*

FUTURA PUBLICATIONS
FICTION
0 7088 3724 7

Futura

THE SUMMERHOUSE

VAL MULKERNS

'A remarkable book, full of insight and feeling . . .'
Evening Press

It crouched forlornly in the kitchen – a crumbling fretwork summerhouse, a symbol of failure and decay, perfectly appropriate to the family that drifted round its disintegrating form, sniping bitchily at each other.

Eleanor, beautiful, frustrated, feeding on her contempt for her spineless husband Con; Margaret, mother of Martin, slowly sinking back into the clinging folds of her family from which she had all too briefly escaped; their mother, senile and overbearing; Hanny, spinster daughter, finding her only satisfaction in eroding her sisters' confidence and self image; and Ruth, Martin's wife, a crisp if timid observer of the lethal family minuet . . .

Told in the voices of five separate but intertwined characters, THE SUMMERHOUSE evokes the lives of an Irish family whose tragedies and occasional joys will haunt every reader.

'evocative' *The Irish Press*

FUTURA PUBLICATIONS
FICTION
0 7088 2623 7

Futura

B.F.P.O. customers please allow 60p for the first book, 25p for the second book plus 15p per copy for the next 7 books, thereafter 9p per book.

Overseas customers including Eire please allow £1.25 for postage and packing for the first book, 75p for the second book and 28p for each subsequent title ordered.